Daily Cumulative Review

Level 3

HOUGHTON MIFFLIN

Boston • Atlanta • Dallas • Denver • Geneva, Illinois • Palo Alto • Princeton

1999 Impression
Copyright © 1994 by Houghton Mifflin Company. All rights reserved.
No Part of this work may be reproduced or transmitted in any form or by any means, electronic or mechanical including photocopying and recording, or by any information storage or retrieval system, unless such copying is expressly permitted by federal copyright law. Address inquires to School Permissions, Houghton Mifflin Company, 222 Berkeley Street, Boston, MA 02116.

Printed in U.S.A.

ISBN: 0-395-86253-1

12 13 14 15 16-B- 06 05 04 03 02 01

Name _____

 DAILY CUMULATIVE REVIEW

Write the missing numbers.

1. 1, _____ , 3, 4, _____

2. 6, _____ , _____ , 9, 10

3. _____ , 12, 13, 14, _____

4. _____ , _____ , 18, 19, 20

5. 1, _____ , 3, _____ , 5, _____ , 7, _____

6. 2, _____ , 4, _____ , 6, _____ , 8, _____

7. 13, _____ , 15, _____ , 17, _____ , 19, _____

8. 7, _____ , 5, _____ , 3, _____ , 1, _____

9. 13, _____ , 11, _____ , 9, _____ , 7, _____

10. 20, _____ , 18, _____ , 16, _____ , 14

Solve.

11. How many days are there in 1 week?   _____

12. How many days are there in this month?   _____

13. How many months are there in 1 year?   _____

Name _____

Write the sum.

1. 1 + 2	**2.** 1 + 9	**3.** 2 + 6	**4.** 4 + 2
5. 5 + 5	**6.** 4 + 4	**7.** 6 + 4	**8.** 5 + 2
9. 3 + 4	**10.** 5 + 3	**11.** 2 + 2	**12.** 8 + 2
13. 4 + 5	**14.** 7 + 2	**15.** 1 + 8	**16.** 3 + 2

Solve.

17. Write three numbers that are between 10 and 20.

_____

18. Write three numbers that are between 50 and 60.

_____

Name _____

Write the missing number.

1.

30 31 ■ 33

2.

67 ■ 69 70

_____   _____

Write the number the arrow is pointing to.

3.

↓

35 36   ■

4.

↓

■   97 98

_____   _____

Write the missing numbers.

5. _____ , 44, _____ , 46, _____ , 48, _____

6. 57, _____ , 59, _____ , 61, _____, 63

7. 16, _____ , 18, _____ , 20, _____, 22

8. _____ , 75, _____ , 77, _____, 79, _____

Solve.

9. Write six numbers that are between 25 and 35.

_____

4 ▸ DAILY CUMULATIVE REVIEW

Write the sum.

1.　　3
　　　　+ 2

2.　　4
　　　　+ 5

3.　　8
　　　　+ 2

4.　　4
　　　　+ 4

5.　　4
　　　　+ 3

6.　　7
　　　　+ 2

7.　　6
　　　　+ 1

8.　　6
　　　　+ 3

9.　　4
　　　　+ 8

10.　　6
　　　　+ 6

11.　　6
　　　　+ 5

12.　　7
　　　　+ 4

13.　　8
　　　　+ 3

14.　　1
　　　　+ 5

15.　　7
　　　　+ 5

16.　　3
　　　　+ 5

Solve.

17. Write a word problem using the addition
fact 4 + 7 = 11.

_____

_____

_____

_____

Name _____

Write the sum.

1. $\begin{array}{r} 5 \\ + 5 \\ \hline \end{array}$ **2.** $\begin{array}{r} 6 \\ + 6 \\ \hline \end{array}$ **3.** $\begin{array}{r} 7 \\ + 7 \\ \hline \end{array}$ **4.** $\begin{array}{r} 8 \\ + 8 \\ \hline \end{array}$

5. $\begin{array}{r} 9 \\ + 9 \\ \hline \end{array}$ **6.** $\begin{array}{r} 10 \\ + 10 \\ \hline \end{array}$ **7.** $\begin{array}{r} 6 \\ + 5 \\ \hline \end{array}$ **8.** $\begin{array}{r} 8 \\ + 4 \\ \hline \end{array}$

9. $\begin{array}{r} 7 \\ + 5 \\ \hline \end{array}$ **10.** $\begin{array}{r} 5 \\ + 8 \\ \hline \end{array}$ **11.** $\begin{array}{r} 9 \\ + 6 \\ \hline \end{array}$ **12.** $\begin{array}{r} 6 \\ + 7 \\ \hline \end{array}$

13. $\begin{array}{r} 8 \\ + 3 \\ \hline \end{array}$ **14.** $\begin{array}{r} 8 \\ + 9 \\ \hline \end{array}$ **15.** $\begin{array}{r} 7 \\ + 8 \\ \hline \end{array}$ **16.** $\begin{array}{r} 4 \\ + 7 \\ \hline \end{array}$

Solve.

17. Artie buys 1 box of cereal and 1 bottle of juice. He gives the clerk $10. How much change should he get back?

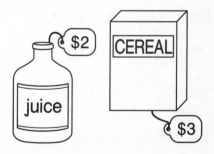

_____

6 DAILY CUMULATIVE REVIEW

Count by 10's. Write the numbers.

1. 20, _____, _____, _____, _____, _____

2. 36, _____, _____, _____, _____, _____

3. 42, _____, _____, _____, _____, _____

4. 15, _____, _____, _____, _____, _____

Count by 5's. Write the numbers.

5. 5, _____, _____, _____, _____, _____

6. 50, _____, _____, _____, _____, _____

7. 35, _____, _____, _____, _____, _____

8. 70, _____, _____, _____, _____, _____

Count by 2's. Write the numbers.

9. 2, _____, _____, _____, _____, _____

10. 32, _____, _____, _____, _____, _____

11. 76, _____, _____, _____, _____, _____

12. 44, _____, _____, _____, _____, _____

7 DAILY CUMULATIVE REVIEW

Write the sum.

1. $7 + 0 =$ _____ **2.** $5 + 6 =$ _____

3. $8 + 7 =$ _____ **4.** $8 + 6 =$ _____

5. $2 + 9 =$ _____ **6.** $6 + 7 =$ _____

7. $9 + 8 =$ _____ **8.** $8 + 3 =$ _____

9. $6 + 9 =$ _____ **10.** $10 + 10 =$ _____

11. $\begin{array}{r} 5 \\ + 8 \\ \hline \end{array}$ **12.** $\begin{array}{r} 7 \\ + 4 \\ \hline \end{array}$ **13.** $\begin{array}{r} 7 \\ + 9 \\ \hline \end{array}$ **14.** $\begin{array}{r} 7 \\ + 7 \\ \hline \end{array}$

15. $\begin{array}{r} 9 \\ + 9 \\ \hline \end{array}$ **16.** $\begin{array}{r} 0 \\ + 9 \\ \hline \end{array}$ **17.** $\begin{array}{r} 7 \\ + 5 \\ \hline \end{array}$ **18.** $\begin{array}{r} 8 \\ + 8 \\ \hline \end{array}$

Solve.

19. Peggy has 2 brothers and 1 sister.
How many children are there in
Peggy's family?

_____

8 ▸ DAILY CUMULATIVE REVIEW

Write the missing numbers.

1. 63, _____ , 65, _____ , 67, _____ , 69, _____

2. 48, _____ , _____ , 51, 52, _____ , _____ , 55

3. _____ , _____ , 27, 28, _____ , _____ , _____ , 32

4. 76, 77, _____ , _____ , _____ , _____ , _____ , 83

5. 13, 14, _____ , _____ , _____ , 18, 19, _____

6. 38, _____ , 36, _____ , _____ , 33, _____ , 31

7. _____ , 90, 89, 88, _____ , _____ , _____ , 84

8. 63, _____ , 61, _____ , 59, _____ , 57, _____

9. 100, _____ , _____ , _____ , 96, 95, _____ , _____

10. _____ , _____ , 83, 82, 81, _____ , _____ , _____

Solve.

11. A memo pad costs 45¢. Keith
has 2 quarters. Is this enough
to buy a memo pad?   _____

9 DAILY CUMULATIVE REVIEW

Write the sum.

1.	3 + 7	2.	5 + 5	3.	8 + 2	4.	1 + 9

5.	5 7 + 3	6.	6 8 + 4	7.	2 6 + 8	8.	6 6 + 3

9.	1 5 + 6	10.	5 7 + 2	11.	1 3 + 9	12.	2 8 + 7

13. $9 + 7 =$ _____   **14.** $6 + 9 =$ _____

15. $5 + 8 + 3 =$ _____   **16.** $4 + 1 + 6 =$ _____

17. $7 + 2 + 1 =$ _____   **18.** $3 + 3 + 8 =$ _____

Solve.

19. Jessica had some quarters. She gave 5 quarters to her brother. She has 6 left. How many quarters did she start with?

_____

10 DAILY CUMULATIVE REVIEW

Write the difference.

1. 9
   -5

2. 8
   -7

3. 13
   $-\ 8$

4. 16
   $-\ 8$

5. 4
   -0

6. 15
   $-\ 6$

7. 14
   $-\ 5$

8. 15
   $-\ 9$

9. $14 - 6 =$ _____

10. $16 - 7 =$ _____

11. $15 - 8 =$ _____

12. $11 - 3 =$ _____

13. $13 - 7 =$ _____

14. $12 - 5 =$ _____

15. $13 - 4 =$ _____

16. $7 - 0 =$ _____

17. $18 - 9 =$ _____

18. $9 - 1 =$ _____

Solve.

19. Joseph has two dogs. Spot eats
    2 pounds of dog food every day. Fido
    eats 1 pound more than Spot. How
    much dog food does Joseph use
    every day?

_____

11 DAILY CUMULATIVE REVIEW

Write the difference.

1. $\begin{array}{r} 16 \\ -\ 8 \\ \hline \end{array}$ **2.** $\begin{array}{r} 18 \\ -\ 9 \\ \hline \end{array}$ **3.** $\begin{array}{r} 10 \\ -\ 6 \\ \hline \end{array}$ **4.** $\begin{array}{r} 5 \\ -\ 0 \\ \hline \end{array}$

5. $\begin{array}{r} 17 \\ -\ 9 \\ \hline \end{array}$ **6.** $\begin{array}{r} 20 \\ -\ 10 \\ \hline \end{array}$ **7.** $\begin{array}{r} 13 \\ -\ 6 \\ \hline \end{array}$ **8.** $\begin{array}{r} 14 \\ -\ 9 \\ \hline \end{array}$

9. $16 - 7 =$ _____   **10.** $15 - 9 =$ _____

11. $11 - 7 =$ _____   **12.** $11 - 2 =$ _____

Complete the number sentence.

13. $3 +$ _____ $= 9$ **14.** $13 = 8 +$ _____

15. _____ $+ 6 = 15$ **16.** $14 =$ _____ $+ 14$

17. $7 +$ _____ $= 10$ **18.** $12 = 8 +$ _____

Solve.

19. Dr. Farzad is planting 12 rose bushes.
She has already planted 7 bushes.
How many more bushes does she have
to plant?

_____

DAILY CUMULATIVE REVIEW

Write the answer.

1. 17
    − 8

2. 8
    + 6

3. 15
    − 7

4. 16
    − 8

5. 9
    + 9

6. 13
    − 7

7. 9
    + 0

8. 11
    − 4

9. 9
    + 7

10. 14
     − 7

11. 4
     + 9

12. 20
     − 10

13. $9 + 8 =$ _____

14. $10 − 7 =$ _____

15. $7 + 7 =$ _____

16. $12 − 7 =$ _____

17. $8 + 3 =$ _____

18. $15 − 6 =$ _____

Solve.

19. Vincent is 7 years younger than his sister, Joanna. Vincent is 8 years old. How old is Joanna?

_____

Name _____

 DAILY CUMULATIVE REVIEW

Write the sum.

1.   7
    + 1

2.   5
    + 10

3.   10
    + 3

4.   1
    + 6

5.   2
    + 10

6.   1
    + 9

7.   9
    + 10

8.   1
    + 8

9.   10
    + 4

10.   10
    + 6

11.   8
    + 10

12.   1
    + 10

Complete the number sentence.

13. 3 + _____ = 5

14. 9 = 8 + _____

15. _____ + 10 = 15

16. 7 + _____ = 10

17. 11 = _____ + 11

18. 13 = 9 + _____

Solve.

19. Hyung builds a model train with 9 cars.
He adds 6 more cars. How many cars
does his model train have now?

_____

14 DAILY CUMULATIVE REVIEW

Write the answer.

1. 9
  + 4

2. 11
   − 2

3. 5
  + 8

4. 17
   − 9

5. 5
  + 9

6. 8
  + 7

7. 20
  − 10

8. 14
   − 7

9. $3 + 9 =$ _____

10. $18 − 9 =$ _____

11. $8 + 8 =$ _____

12. $10 − 2 =$ _____

Solve each problem.

13. Lori lost 4 baseball cards. Now she has 7 left. How many did she start with?

_____

14. Ding Wei has 9 baseball cards. He buys 7 more. How many cards does he have now?

_____

15. A pack of cards costs 59¢. Lisa has 2 quarters. Does she have enough money?

_____

16. Marty has 8 cards. His brother has 4 cards. How many cards do they have in all?

_____

15 **DAILY CUMULATIVE REVIEW**

Write a fact family for the number sentence.

1. 3 + 7 = 10

_____

_____

_____

2. 8 + 3 = 11

_____

_____

_____

3. 3 + 9 = 12

_____

_____

_____

4. 5 + 8 = 13

_____

_____

_____

5. 8 + 6 = 14

_____

_____

_____

6. 8 + 7 = 15

_____

_____

_____

Solve.

7. Doreen, Sheila, David, and Jerry each have 4 dinosaur models. David gives 1 of his models to Jerry. Sheila gives 2 of her models to Doreen. How many models do they have in all?

_____

16 ▸ DAILY CUMULATIVE REVIEW

Write the sum.

1.	7	2.	8	3.	5	4.	6
	+ 7		+ 7		+ 5		+ 5

5.	4	6.	4	7.	3	8.	3
	+ 4		+ 5		+ 3		+ 4

9.	6	10.	7	11.	8	12.	9
	+ 6		+ 6		+ 8		+ 8

Write the missing numbers.

13. 94, _____ , 96 , _____, 98, _____, _____

14. _____, _____, 69, _____, 71, _____

15. 54, 53, _____, _____, 50, _____, _____

Solve.

16. Antonia wants to buy a box
of computer disks that costs
$13. She has $8. How much
more money does she need?   _____

Name _____

Write the sum.

1.	4	**2.**	9	**3.**	6	**4.**	7
	7		5		6		5
	+ 8		+ 3		+ 5		+ 5

Complete the number sentence.

5. $3 + \underline{\hspace{1cm}} = 10$ **6.** $13 = 7 + \underline{\hspace{1cm}}$

7. $\underline{\hspace{1cm}} + 7 = 11$ **8.** $15 = \underline{\hspace{1cm}} + 7$

9. $9 + \underline{\hspace{1cm}} = 12$ **10.** $16 = 8 + \underline{\hspace{1cm}}$

11. $17 = 9 + \underline{\hspace{1cm}}$ **12.** $8 + \underline{\hspace{1cm}} = 11$

13. $6 + \underline{\hspace{1cm}} = 14$ **14.** $13 = \underline{\hspace{1cm}} + 4$

Solve each problem.

15. Vera promised to sell 15 tickets to the concert. She has already sold 6 tickets. How many more must she sell?

_____

16. Geraldo promised to sell 12 tickets to the concert. He has 5 tickets left. How many tickets has he sold already?

_____

18 DAILY CUMULATIVE REVIEW

Write a fact family for the number sentence.

1. $4 + 7 = 11$ **2.** $6 + 9 = 15$

_____   _____

_____   _____

_____   _____

Write the sum.

3. $9 + 0 =$ _____   **4.** $6 + 0 =$ _____

5. $0 + 100 =$ _____   **6.** $0 + 78 =$ _____

7.   6   **8.**   4   **9.**   4   **10.**   5
          2   3   4   7
          5   7   8   1
       $+ 3$ $+ 1$ $+ 3$ $+ 3$

Solve each problem.

11. Henri needs 14 shells for his art project. He has 8 shells. How many more shells does he need?

_____

12. Maxine needs 10 shells for her project. She has 6 shells. How many more shells does she need?

_____

Name _____

Write the answer.

1.	**2.**	**3.**	**4.**
5	1	6	3
7	8	5	2
+ 3	+ 7	+ 2	+ 9

5.	**6.**	**7.**	**8.**
7	14	11	12
− 0	− 5	− 3	− 5

Write the missing numbers.

9. 17, 18, _____, _____, _____, 22, _____

10. 88, _____, _____, _____, 92, _____, 94

11. 26, _____, _____, 29, _____, _____, 32

12. 40, _____, 38, _____, 36, _____, _____

Solve.

13. Maria baked 8 loaves of bread for the bake sale. Jeff baked 6 loaves and David baked 9. How many loaves of bread did they have in all?   _____

Name _____

Write the number the arrow is pointing to.

1.
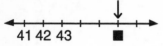
41 42 43 ■

_____

2.
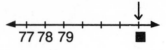
77 78 79 ■

_____

3.
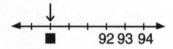
■ 92 93 94

_____

4.
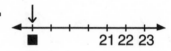
■ 21 22 23

_____

Write the missing sign.

5. $7 + 6 = 7 + 7 \bigcirc 1$ **6.** $7 + 8 = 7 + 7 \bigcirc 1$

7. $9 + 8 = 9 + 9 \bigcirc 1$ **8.** $5 + 6 = 5 + 5 \bigcirc 1$

Use the double to write the sum.

9. $13 + 13 = 26$ **10.** $11 + 11 = 22$

$12 + 13 =$ _____ $12 + 11 =$ _____

Solve.

11. Marsha has 8 books. April
has 1 more. How many books
do they have together?   _____

Name _____

Write the answer. Use mental math when you can.

1. 9
   + 8

2. 19
   + 8

3. 5
   + 9

4. 15
   + 9

5. 15
   − 9

6. 25
   − 9

7. 2
   + 9

8. 12
   + 9

9. 9
   + 7

10. 19
    + 7

11. 12
    − 9

12. 22
    − 9

Write a fact family for the number sentence.

13. 6 + 0 = 6

14. 6 + 7 = 13

_____   _____

_____   _____

_____   _____

Solve.

15. Pablo has 8 buttons. He buys 3 more at a flea market and 5 more at a button swap. How many buttons does he have now?   _____

22 DAILY CUMULATIVE REVIEW

Complete the number sentence.

1. 82 = _____ tens + _____ ones

2. 37 = _____ tens + _____ ones

3. 90 = _____ tens + _____ ones

4. 903 = _____ hundreds + _____ tens + _____ ones

5. 770 = _____ hundreds + _____ tens + _____ ones

6. 400 = _____ hundreds + _____ tens + _____ ones

Write the answer.

7. 20 − 10 = _____   **8.** 15 − 8 = _____

9. 4 + 7 = _____   **10.** 12 − 0 = _____

11. 16 − 9 = _____   **12.** 8 + 6 = _____

Solve.

13. Arthur wants to put 12 plants in a flower box. He has 4 ivy plants and 4 geranium plants. How many more plants should he buy?

_____

Name _____

23 DAILY CUMULATIVE REVIEW

Write the sum.

1. $3 + 0 + 8 = $ _____
2. $6 + 3 + 3 = $ _____
3. $3 + 7 + 9 = $ _____
4. $8 + 2 + 4 = $ _____
5. $1 + 9 + 4 = $ _____
6. $5 + 9 + 4 = $ _____

Write the digit that is in the tens place.

7. 170 _____
8. 298 _____
9. 513 _____
10. 409 _____
11. 725 _____
12. 964 _____

Write the value of the digit 2.

13. 927 _____
14. 283 _____
15. 280 _____
16. 142 _____
17. 892 _____
18. 327 _____

Solve.

19. Mary is thinking of a number. It is between 40 and 50. If you add the digits, the sum is 10. What is Mary's number? _____

Name _____

Write the answer. Use mental math.

1.	60	2.	400	3.	7000
	+ 20		+ 500		+ 6000

4.	80	5.	900	6.	11,000
	− 30		− 200		− 3,000

In which place is the digit 3? Write *ones*, *tens*, or *hundreds*.

7. 305   8. 13

_____   _____

9. 539   10. 1631

_____   _____

Solve.

11. Mac has collected 40 T-shirts for the clothing drive. Junior has collected 30 and Martha has collected 20. How many T-shirts do they have so far? _____

25 ⏵ DAILY CUMULATIVE REVIEW

Write the missing sign.

1. $9 + 8 = 9 + 9 \bigcirc 1$

2. $14 + 13 = 14 + 14 \bigcirc 1$

3. $10 + 11 = 10 + 10 \bigcirc 1$

4. $16 + 15 = 16 + 16 \bigcirc 1$

5. $12 + 13 = 12 + 12 \bigcirc 1$

Write the number in standard form.

6. $4000 + 300 + 20 + 7$ _____

7. $1000 + 400 + 2$ _____

8. three thousand five hundred one _____

9. seven thousand two _____

Solve. Use the digits 3, 9, 6, and 5.

10. What is the greatest number you can write? _____

11. What is the least number you can write? _____

Name _____

Write < or >.

1. 43 ◯ 74   **2.** 86 ◯ 68

3. 603 ◯ 630   **4.** 745 ◯ 689

5. 923 ◯ 856   **6.** 1987 ◯ 1990

7. 909 ◯ 901   **8.** 7693 ◯ 3967

Order from least to greatest.

9. 60, 24, 17   _____

10. 309, 247, 485   _____

11. 870, 708, 304   _____

12. 1263, 6231, 3612   _____

Solve.

13. Write six numbers that are between 495 and 595.

_____

14. Write six numbers that are between 8093 and 9038.

_____

27 DAILY CUMULATIVE REVIEW

Write the difference.

1. $15 - 0 =$ _____   **2.** $12 - 7 =$ _____

3. $17 - 8 =$ _____   **4.** $13 - 6 =$ _____

5. $14 - 9 =$ _____   **6.** $16 - 8 =$ _____

Write the sum.

7.	9	**8.**	8	**9.**	6	**10.**	3
	6		6		7		7
	+ 4		+ 5		+ 8		+ 8

11.	4	**12.**	3	**13.**	4	**14.**	2
	6		5		7		7
	7		2		8		5
	+ 3		+ 4		+ 6		+ 4

Solve.

15. Alonzo wants to buy a toy
that costs $2. He has a
one-dollar bill, 2 quarters,
3 dimes, and 5 nickels. Does
he have enough money to
buy the toy?   _____

Write the answer. Use mental math.

1. 40 + 50   **2.** 90 + 70

_____   _____

3. 110 – 80   **4.** 800 + 500

_____   _____

5. 1500 – 600   **6.** 2000 – 500

_____   _____

Write the money amount. Use a dollar sign and decimal point.

7.    **8.**

_____   _____

9. 35 dollars and 68 cents   _____

10. 20 dollars and 32 cents   _____

11. sixteen dollars and fourteen cents   _____

12. twenty-seven dollars and thirty cents _____

13. eleven dollars and seventy-six cents _____

Name _____

Tell two ways to pay the amount without using pennies.

1. 40¢ _____

_____

2. 75¢ _____

_____

3. 65¢ _____

_____

Write the number in standard form.

4. 2000 + 30 + 6 _____

5. 6000 + 700 + 80 + 4 _____

6. 7 thousands + 1 ten + 9 ones _____

7. 2 thousands + 6 hundreds + 5 ones _____

8. one thousand three hundred four _____

Solve.

9. Rosa buys a book for $1.25.
She pays $2.00. How much
change does she get? _____

Name _____

Write the missing numbers.

1. 52, _____, _____, 55

2. _____, _____, 380, 381

3. 499, _____, _____, 502

4. 999, _____, _____, 1002

5. _____, _____, 7000, 7001

Write the answer. Use mental math.

6.   500
      + 500

7.   700
      + 600

8.   1100
      − 400

9.   6000
      + 3000

10.   5000
      + 2000

11.   8000
      − 3000

Solve.

12. What is Meg's number? It is an even number between 40 and 60. If you add its digits, the sum is 7.

_____

Name _____

31 DAILY CUMULATIVE REVIEW

In which place is the digit 8? Write *ones*, *tens*, or *hundreds*.

1. 982

2. 5208

_____

_____

3. 812

4. 738

_____

_____

Complete the number sentence.

5. $7 + \underline{\hspace{1cm}} = 7$

6. $10 = 4 + \underline{\hspace{1cm}}$

7. $\underline{\hspace{1cm}} + 8 = 14$

8. $9 + \underline{\hspace{1cm}} = 18$

9. $4 + \underline{\hspace{1cm}} = 12$

10. $14 = 7 + \underline{\hspace{1cm}}$

11. $19 = \underline{\hspace{1cm}} + 9$

12. $\underline{\hspace{1cm}} + 10 = 20$

13. $12 = 6 + \underline{\hspace{1cm}}$

14. $15 = \underline{\hspace{1cm}} + 6$

Solve.

15. What is Bobby's number? It is between 15 and 25. If you subtract the tens digit from the ones digit, the difference is 8.

_____

32 DAILY CUMULATIVE REVIEW

Write the time.

1.

_____

2.

_____

3.

_____

4.

_____

5.

_____

6.

_____

Solve each problem.

7. Alice gave the clerk $1. She got 15¢ change. How much did Alice spend?

_____

8. Todd gave the clerk $2. He got 25¢ change. How much did Todd spend?

_____

9. Connie paid $2 for a book. She got 51¢ change. How much did the book cost?

_____

Name _____

Write < or >.

1. 89 ◯ 91

2. 502 ◯ 520

3. 637 ◯ 376

4. 1000 ◯ 999

5. 2047 ◯ 2470

6. 4560 ◯ 6054

Write whether it is *A.M.* or *P.M.* when you do each.

7. wake up _____

8. eat your dinner _____

9. go to school _____

10. eat your breakfast _____

11. go home after school _____

Solve.

12. There are 9 rooms on the first floor of a two-story building. The second floor has 2 more rooms than the first floor. How many rooms are there in the building? _____

34 **DAILY CUMULATIVE REVIEW**

Write the sum.

1.	7	2.	6	3.	8	4.	1
	5		6		4		6
	+ 3		+ 4		+ 8		+ 9

5.	2	6.	5	7.	5	8.	3
	3		9		8		6
	+ 6		+ 4		+ 4		+ 7

Write the number in standard form.

9. three thousand two hundred forty   _____

10. six hundred eight   _____

11. one thousand five hundred seventy   _____

12. six thousand five   _____

Solve.

13. Mike needs 20 leaves for his science project. He has collected 10. How many more leaves does Mike need?   _____

35 DAILY CUMULATIVE REVIEW

Write the missing numbers.

1. 99, _____, 101, _____, 103, _____

2. 35, _____, _____, 38, _____, _____

3. _____, 61, 62, _____, _____, _____, 66

Write the double you could use to find the sum. Then write the sum.

4.
$$+ \underline{} \qquad \begin{array}{r} 8 \\ + 9 \\ \hline \end{array}$$

5.
$$+ \underline{} \qquad \begin{array}{r} 4 \\ + 5 \\ \hline \end{array}$$

6.
$$+ \underline{} \qquad \begin{array}{r} 5 \\ + 6 \\ \hline \end{array}$$

7.
$$+ \underline{} \qquad \begin{array}{r} 6 \\ + 7 \\ \hline \end{array}$$

8.
$$+ \underline{} \qquad \begin{array}{r} 3 \\ + 4 \\ \hline \end{array}$$

9.
$$+ \underline{} \qquad \begin{array}{r} 8 \\ + 7 \\ \hline \end{array}$$

Solve.

10. Barbara built 8 bluebird houses for the nature sale. Jeff built 6 and Al built 9. How many did they build in all?

_____

36 DAILY CUMULATIVE REVIEW

Write the time.

1.

_____

2.

_____

3.

_____

4.

_____

5.

_____

6.

_____

Write the correct change.

7. $1.00 paid for a pad that cost 89¢. _____

8. $2.00 paid for a book that cost $1.95. _____

9. $1.00 paid for a marker that cost 66¢. _____

10. $1.50 paid for a pen that cost $1.37. _____

11. $1.50 paid for a snack that cost $1.29. _____

12. $2.00 paid for a scarf that cost $1.40. _____

Name _____

Write < or >.

1. 49 ◯ 94
2. 101 ◯ 99
3. 340 ◯ 304
4. 919 ◯ 991
5. 218 ◯ 812
6. 1083 ◯ 1308
7. 7532 ◯ 7325
8. 8776 ◯ 6778

Write the difference.

9. 13
− 6

10. 15
− 9

11. 17
− 8

12. 12
− 4

13. 16
− 8

14. 12
− 5

15. 15
− 7

16. 11
− 3

Solve each problem.

17. Maureen gave the clerk $2.
She got 41¢ change. How
much did she spend?   _____

18. Tony gave the clerk $1.50.
He got 16¢ change. How
much did he spend?   _____

Name _____

Write a fact family for the number sentence.

1. $5 + 8 = 13$ **2.** $8 + 6 = 14$

_____   _____

_____   _____

_____   _____

3. $9 + 3 = 12$ **4.** $6 + 5 = 11$

_____   _____

_____   _____

_____   _____

Write the value of the digit 7.

5. 167 _____   **6.** 745 _____

7. 279 _____   **8.** 974 _____

9. 527 _____   **10.** 701 _____

Solve.

11. What is Debby's number?
It is an odd number between
120 and 130. If you add its
digits, the sum is 6.   _____

39 ▸ DAILY CUMULATIVE REVIEW

Write the sum. Use mental math.

1.	5	**2.**	15	**3.**	8	**4.**	18
	+ 1		+ 1		+ 10		+ 10

5.	3	**6.**	13	**7.**	9	**8.**	19
	+ 10		+ 10		+ 1		+ 1

Order from least to greatest.

9. 38, 83, 80, 33 _____

10. 901, 119, 191 _____

11. 435, 340, 543 _____

12. 1608, 186, 168, 1806 _____

Solve. Write A.M. or P.M. in your answer.

13. Teddy's soccer game lasted 2 hours. It started at 10:30 A.M. What time did it end?

_____

14. Erin's softball game lasted 2 hours. It started at 11:00 A.M. What time did it end?

_____

40 DAILY CUMULATIVE REVIEW

Tell whether it is *A.M.* or *P.M.* when you do each.

1. eat breakfast _____

2. eat dinner _____

3. get dressed for school _____

4. do your homework _____

Write the sum.

5.   68
    + 41

6.   95
    + 28

7. $0.59
   + 0.77

8.   276
   + 346

9.   489
   + 302

10.   156 mi
   + 57 mi

Solve each problem.

11. Inez wants to buy a watch that costs $14. She has $6. How much more money does she need?

_____

12. Lance wants to buy a radio that costs $11. He has $8. How much more money does he need?

_____

41 DAILY CUMULATIVE REVIEW

Tell two ways to pay the amount without using pennies.

1. $1.15 _____

_____

2. $1.60 _____

_____

Write the sum.

3. $2 + 8 + 6 + 1 =$ _____

4. $3 + 8 + 1 + 6 =$ _____

5. $4 + 7 + 3 + 5 =$ _____

6. $1 + 8 + 2 + 9 =$ _____

7. $6 + 4 + 2 + 7 =$ _____

Solve each problem.

8. Ed has 2 quarters, 1 dime, and 3 nickels. Does he have enough money to buy a 59¢ toy?

_____

9. Pia has 6 dimes, 5 nickels, and 4 pennies. Does she have enough money to pay $1.09 for a snack?

_____

42 DAILY CUMULATIVE REVIEW

Complete the number sentence.

1. $14 = 7 + \underline{\hspace{2cm}}$

2. $6 + \underline{\hspace{2cm}} = 15$

3. $8 + \underline{\hspace{2cm}} = 12$

4. $9 + \underline{\hspace{2cm}} = 13$

5. $15 = \underline{\hspace{2cm}} + 5$

6. $\underline{\hspace{2cm}} + 8 = 16$

7. $4 + \underline{\hspace{2cm}} = 11$

8. $10 = 5 + \underline{\hspace{2cm}}$

9. $17 = 8 + \underline{\hspace{2cm}}$

10. $\underline{\hspace{2cm}} + 25 = 25$

Write the digit that is in the hundreds place.

11. 987 _____

12. 2507 _____

13. 5368 _____

14. 296 _____

15. 146 _____

16. 3402 _____

17. 7840 _____

18. 2845 _____

Solve.

19. Mr. Garcia made 15 sandwiches for the picnic. He ate 2 and gave 4 to his sons. How many sandwiches are left? _____

43 DAILY CUMULATIVE REVIEW

Write the sum.

1. $\begin{array}{r} 86 \\ + 46 \\ \hline \end{array}$ **2.** $\begin{array}{r} 37 \\ + 63 \\ \hline \end{array}$ **3.** $\begin{array}{r} 12 \\ + 39 \\ \hline \end{array}$ **4.** $\begin{array}{r} 28 \\ + 54 \\ \hline \end{array}$

5. $18 + 52 =$ _____   **6.** $45 + 36 =$ _____

7. $91 + 19 =$ _____   **8.** $70 + 49 =$ _____

9. $66 + 41 =$ _____   **10.** $55 + 68 =$ _____

Complete the number sentence.

11. $84 =$ _____ tens + _____ ones

12. $726 =$ _____ hundreds + _____ tens + _____ ones

13. $803 =$ _____ hundreds + _____ tens + _____ ones

14. $260 =$ _____ hundreds + _____ tens + _____ ones

15. $635 =$ _____ hundreds + _____ tens + _____ ones

Solve.

16. Sam is 6 years older than his sister, Hilda. Hilda is 9 years old. How old is Sam? _____

Name _____

Write the difference.

| 1. | 44 | 2. | 62 | 3. | $0.75 |
| | − 17 | | − 26 | | − 0.49 |

| 4. | 53 | 5. | 87 | 6. | 54 yd |
| | − 38 | | − 60 | | − 15 yd |

**Write the money amount. Use a dollar
sign and decimal point in your answer.**

7. seven dollars and ninety cents _____

8. 8 dollars and 62 cents _____

9. twelve dollars and three cents _____

10. 17 dollars and 71 cents _____

Solve.

11. The chart shows
the final score of a
basketball game.
Which team won?
By how many
points did the
winning team win?

HOME TEAM	VISITORS
8 5	5 9

Name _____

Write the correct change.

1. $1.00 paid for a 45¢ comb. _____

2. $1.00 paid for a 39¢ ruler. _____

3. $1.50 paid for a $1.27 notebook. _____

4. $2.00 paid for a paintbrush that
cost $1.19. _____

Write the number the arrow is pointing to.

5.

_____

6.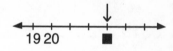

_____

7.

_____

8.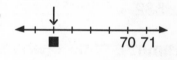

_____

Solve.

9. Marvin bought a dozen eggs.
He used three for breakfast
and two for lunch. How many
eggs are left? _____

Name _____

Write the difference.

1.   791
       − 25

2. $8.32
       − 5.74

3.   555
       − 98

4.   396
       − 159

5. $2.57
       − 1.59

6.   335 mi
       − 79 mi

Write the value of the digit 3.

7. 703 _____

8. 3529 _____

9. 8319 _____

10. 2531 _____

11. 3642 _____

12. 396 _____

13. 532 _____

14. 4703 _____

Estimate. Which two numbers in the box have a sum of:

15. about 500?

429	147
555	361

_____

16. about 700?

17. about 800?

_____   _____

47 DAILY CUMULATIVE REVIEW

Write the number in standard form.

1. seven hundred seven _____

2. two thousand forty-six _____

3. 7 thousands + 5 hundreds + 8 ones _____

4. 3 thousands + 4 ones _____

Write the answer.

5.	**6.**	**7.**	**8.**
8	9	6	5
6	4	3	8
+ 3	+ 5	+ 7	+ 2

9.	**10.**	**11.**	**12.**
16	20	12	15
− 9	− 8	− 7	− 6

Solve each problem.

13. James gave the clerk $2. He got 95¢ change. How much did he spend?

_____

14. Tiffany gave the clerk $2. She got 35¢ change. How much did she spend?

_____

48 DAILY CUMULATIVE REVIEW

Complete the number sentence.

1. $5 + \underline{\hspace{1cm}} = 14$ **2.** $17 = 9 + \underline{\hspace{1cm}}$

3. $\underline{\hspace{1cm}} + 7 = 10$ **4.** $9 + \underline{\hspace{1cm}} = 16$

5. $11 = \underline{\hspace{1cm}} + 3$ **6.** $13 = 6 + \underline{\hspace{1cm}}$

7. $\underline{\hspace{1cm}} + 7 = 12$ **8.** $9 = 9 + \underline{\hspace{1cm}}$

Write a fact family for the number sentence.

9. $5 + 9 = 14$ **10.** $8 + 7 = 15$

_____   _____

_____   _____

_____   _____

Solve. Write *A.M.* or *P.M.* in your answer.

11. The school show lasts for one
and one-half hours. It starts at
7:30 P.M. When does it finish?   _____

12. Swimming practice lasts for
two hours. It ends at 5:00 P.M.
When does it start?   _____

49 ⬧ DAILY CUMULATIVE REVIEW

Write the sum.

1.
```
   18
   54
+ 36
```

2.
```
   39
   44
+  5
```

3.
```
  67 ft
  23 ft
+ 27 ft
```

4.
```
   41
   25
+ 19
```

5.
```
   91
   14
+  8
```

6.
```
  46 mi
  33 mi
+ 57 mi
```

Solve. Use models to help you.

7. Marco has 9 pencils. His sister Janet has 3. How many pencils must Marco give Janet so that they have the same number?

_____

8. Roberta and Alex each have 5 stickers. Roberta gives Alex 2 stickers. How many more stickers than Roberta does Alex have now?

_____

9. Helene folds a piece of paper in half 3 times. How many sections will there be when she opens it up?

_____

50 ◤ DAILY CUMULATIVE REVIEW

Write the sum.

1.	270 + 350	2.	458 + 125	3.	392 + 664

4.	849 + 278	5.	198 + 607	6.	532 + 374

7.	$5.86 + 2.49	8.	$9.75 + 0.88	9.	$4.29 + 3.89

Write the time.

10. **11.**  **12.**

_____

13. **14.** **15.**

_____

51 DAILY CUMULATIVE REVIEW

Tell two ways to pay the amount without using pennies.

1. 50¢ _____

_____

2. 35¢ _____

_____

3. 85¢ _____

_____

Write < or >.

4. 209 ◯ 290

5. 395 ◯ 387

6. 679 ◯ 706

7. 9080 ◯ 8009

8. 2901 ◯ 2019

9. 3799 ◯ 3800

Solve.

10. What is Carmen's number?
It is an even number between
100 and 110. If you add its
digits, the sum is 9. _____

52 DAILY CUMULATIVE REVIEW

Order from least to greatest.

1. 999, 1001, 199 _____

2. 8387, 3783, 3378 _____

3. 9092, 9209, 9029 _____

Write the sum.

4.	46 yd	**5.**	91	**6.**	166
	72 yd		53		777
	+ 85 yd		+ 489		+ 891

Estimate. Write *yes* or *no*.

7. Did Sam sell at least 1000 pair on Monday and Tuesday?

_____

8. Did Sam sell at least 2000 pair in the 5 days?

_____

Sam's Sock Shop	
Day	Pairs Sold
Monday	654
Tuesday	298
Wednesday	890
Thursday	636
Friday	700

9. Did Sam sell more than 3000 pair in the 5 days? _____

53 **DAILY CUMULATIVE REVIEW**

Make a rough front-end estimate. Then adjust.

1. 137
    + 129

2. 899
    + 386

3. 423
    + 984

4. 802
    + 614

5. $1.39
    + 4.15

6. $2.50
    + 3.59

Write the missing sign.

7. $21 + 20 = 21 + 21 \bigcirc 1$

8. $300 + 301 = 300 + 300 \bigcirc 1$

9. $249 + 250 = 250 + 250 \bigcirc 1$

10. $999 + 1000 = 999 + 999 \bigcirc 1$

Solve.

11. Jennifer buys bananas for $1.38. She pays with 2 one-dollar bills. The clerk gives Jennifer 2 quarters, 1 dime, and 2 pennies. Is this the correct change? _____

54 DAILY CUMULATIVE REVIEW

Write the answer. Use mental math.

1. $40 + 50 =$ _____   **2.** $90 + 70 =$ _____

3. $110 - 80 =$ _____   **4.** $800 + 500 =$ _____

5. $30 + 70 =$ _____   **6.** $200 + 500 =$ _____

Estimate. Which two numbers in the box have a difference of:

7. about 100?

371	501
281	895

_____

8. about 200?   **9.** about 500?

_____   _____

Solve. Write A.M. or P.M. in your answer.

10. Mike reads for one-half hour.
He starts at 4:30 P.M. When
does he finish?   _____

11. Latisha plays softball for
2 hours. She starts at
11:15 A.M. When does she
finish?   _____

55 DAILY CUMULATIVE REVIEW

Write the difference.

1.   72
     − 49

2.   46
     − 21

3. $0.75
     − 0.43

4.   54
     − 30

5.   84
     − 57

6. $0.86
     − 0.38

7.   63
     − 27

8.   98
     − 49

9. $0.90
     − 0.45

Write the missing numbers.

10. 95, _____, _____, 98, _____, _____, 101

11. 899, _____, _____, 902, _____, _____, 905

12. 4996, 4997, _____, _____, 5000, _____

Solve.

13. Mr. Pak has to drive 150 miles
    to visit his mother. He drives
    68 miles and stops for
    20 minutes to have a snack.
    How many more miles does
    he have to drive?   _____

56 DAILY CUMULATIVE REVIEW

Write the difference.

1.   490
      − 225

2.   806
      − 427

3. $5.80
      − 3.72

4.   609
      − 248

5.   390
      − 108

6.   700 mi
      − 356 mi

Use the pictograph to solve each problem.

Books Read This Year

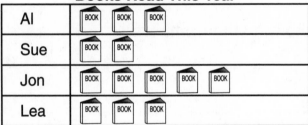

Key: [BOOK] = 5 books

7. How many books did Sue read? _____

8. How many children read 15 books or more? _____

9. Who read the greatest number of books? _____

10. How many more books did Jon read than Sue? _____

Name _____

Write the sum.

1.	323	**2.**	244	**3.**	516
	109		369		351
	+ 216		+ 293		+ 284

4.	550	**5.**	184	**6.**	720
	187		507		697
	+ 896		+ 740		+ 348

Use the number line to answer each question.

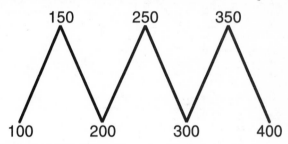

7. What number is halfway between 300 and 400? _____

8. Is 195 closer to 100 or 200? _____

9. Does 339 round to 300 or 400? _____

10. Does 250 round to 200 or 300? _____

11. Does 145 round to 100 or 200? _____

Name _____

Write the answer.

1. 39
     + 48

2. $6.08
     + 9.18

3. 719
     − 138

4. $5.11
     − 2.94

5. $3.83
     + 5.25

6. 305
     − 59

Use the graph to solve each problem.

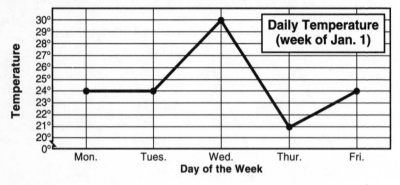

7. Which day had the highest temperature?

_____

8. Was it warmer on Tuesday or Thursday?

_____

9. On how many days was the temperature 24°?

_____

10. How much cooler was it on Thursday than Wednesday?

_____

Name _____

In which place is the digit 6? Write
ones, tens, hundreds,* or *thousands.

1. 564   **2.** 806

_____   _____

3. 4685   **4.** 6092

_____   _____

Circle the letter of the closest estimate.

5.	732	**6.**	966	**7.**	$6.48
	− 348		− 855		− 1.29

5.
  a. 100
  b. 300
  c. 400

6.
  a. 10
  b. 100
  c. 1000

7.
  a. $4
  b. $5
  c. $7

Solve.

8. Write four numbers that are between
890 and 908.

_____

9. Write four numbers that are greater
than 1095.

_____

Name _____

Write the value of the coins.

1.

_____

2.

_____

Write > or <.

3. 607 ◯ 590   **4.** 856 ◯ 865

5. 1045 ◯ 1025   **6.** 2078 ◯ 2068

7. 1001 ◯ 995   **8.** 6750 ◯ 7565

Circle the letter of the choice that correctly answers the question.

9. Last year the Lean Lions lost
3 basketball games by more than
10 points. They lost 4 games by
fewer than 10 points. They also won
6 games. How many games did the
Lean Lions lose?

  a. They played 13 games.

  b. They lost 7 games.

  c. They lost more games than they won.

DAILY CUMULATIVE REVIEW

Write the time.

1.   **2.**   **3.**

_____   _____   _____

Use the table to solve each problem.

4. Ken sold pens to earn money for a class trip. On which two days was Ken's total about $6.00?

Ken's Pen Sales	
Day	**Amount**
Monday	$3.75
Tuesday	$5.25
Wednesday	$2.50
Thursday	$7.75

_____

_____

5. On which two days was Ken's total about $13.00?

_____

6. What was Ken's total sales for four days?

_____

62 DAILY CUMULATIVE REVIEW

Complete the number sentence.

1. 95 = ____ tens + ____ ones

2. 308 = ____ hundreds + ____ tens + ____ ones

3. 490 = ____ hundreds + ____ tens + ____ ones

4. 945 = ____ hundreds + ____ tens + ____ ones

Estimate. Which two numbers in the box have a sum of:

5. about 700?

225	110
682	486

_____

6. about 900?   **7.** about 800?

_____   _____

Solve each problem.

8. Maria has 4 dollar bills, 5 quarters, 4 dimes, 6 nickels, and 3 pennies. Write the amount of money Maria has.

9. Percy has 3 dollar bills, 2 quarters, and 9 pennies. Keith has 35¢ less than Percy. Write the amount of money Keith has.

_____   _____

Name _____

 63 **DAILY CUMULATIVE REVIEW**

Write a fact family for the number sentence.

1. $9 + 7 = 16$ **2.** $6 + 7 = 13$

_____   _____

_____   _____

_____   _____

Write the sum. Use mental math when you can.

3.   725
    + 188

4.   56
    + 765

5. $3.90
    + 4.65

6.   906
    + 190

7.   655
    + 298

8. $0.45
    + 2.95

Solve. Write A.M. or P.M. in your answer.

9. Igor wakes up at 6:30 A.M.
He leaves for school one and
one-half hours later. What time
does Igor leave for school? _____

64 DAILY CUMULATIVE REVIEW

Tell two different ways to pay the amount without using pennies.

1. 80¢ _____

_____

2. $1.45 _____

_____

Write the difference. Use mental math when you can.

3.   890
      − 65

4.   775
      − 290

5. $5.50
      − 0.75

6.   140
      − 70

7.   98
      − 69

8. $9.25
      − 2.50

Solve.

9. Inez has one $5 bill. She buys her sister a poster for $4.55. What change does Inez receive?   _____

65 ▸ DAILY CUMULATIVE REVIEW

Count by 5's. Write the numbers.

1. 5, 10, 15, _____ , _____ , _____ , _____ , _____

2. 75, 80, 85, _____ , _____ , _____ , _____ , _____

Count by 10's. Write the numbers.

3. 60, 70, 80, _____ , _____ , _____ , _____ , _____

4. 210, 220, _____ , _____ , _____ , _____ , _____

Use the pictograph to solve each problem.

Class Science Projects	
Volcanoes	☺ ☺ ☺
Taste-testing	☺ ☺
Plant Growth	☺ ☺
Magnets	☺ ☺ ☺ ☺

Key ☺ = 5 students

5. What type of science project was the most popular?

_____

6. How many more students did projects about volcanoes than about plants?

_____

Name _____

Write the product.

1. $2 \times 1 =$ _____

2. $5 \times 2 =$ _____

3. $4 \times 2 =$ _____

4. $2 \times 5 =$ _____

5. $3 \times 2 =$ _____

6. $6 \times 2 =$ _____

Use the graph to solve each problem.

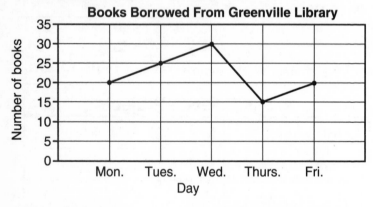

Books Borrowed From Greenville Library

7. On which day were 25 books borrowed from the library?

_____

8. How many books were borrowed from the library on Monday?

_____

9. On which two days were the same number of books borrowed?

_____

DAILY CUMULATIVE REVIEW ....

Write the time.

1.

2.

3.

_____   _____   _____

4.

5.

6.

_____   _____   _____

Write the quotient.

7. $8 \div 2 =$ _____   **8.** $10 \div 2 =$ _____

9. $2 \div 2 =$ _____   **10.** $4 \div 2 =$ _____

11. $6 \div 2 =$ _____   **12.** $8 \div 2 =$ _____

Solve.

13. Kim has 6 flowers. She
wants to share them equally
among 3 friends. How many
flowers will she give each
friend?   _____

68 DAILY CUMULATIVE REVIEW

Write the answer.

1. $\begin{array}{r} 4 \\ \times\,3 \\ \hline \end{array}$ **2.** $\begin{array}{r} 5 \\ \times\,3 \\ \hline \end{array}$ **3.** $\begin{array}{r} 6 \\ \times\,2 \\ \hline \end{array}$ **4.** $\begin{array}{r} 3 \\ \times\,3 \\ \hline \end{array}$

5. $15 \div 3 =$ _____   **6.** $9 \div 3 =$ _____

7. $6 \div 3 =$ _____   **8.** $3 \div 3 =$ _____

Use the graph to solve each problem.

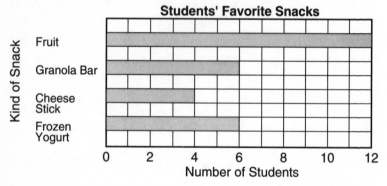

Students' Favorite Snacks

9. Which snack was the most popular?

_____

10. Which snack did the fewest students choose?

_____

11. How many students chose frozen yogurt as their favorite snack?

_____

DAILY CUMULATIVE REVIEW

Write the answer.

1.   4
   × 4

2.   5
   × 4

3.   5
   × 5

4.   4
   × 3

5.   3
   × 3

6.   5
   × 1

7.   2
   × 4

8.   5
   × 3

9. $15 \div 3 =$ _____

10. $20 \div 5 =$ _____

11. $12 \div 4 =$ _____

12. $16 \div 4 =$ _____

Solve each problem. If there is not enough information, tell what you need to know.

13. Bert is making 5 scrapbooks. For each book, he uses 3 pieces of yarn to bind together its pages. How many pieces of yarn will he need?

_____

14. Tanya had 16 stamps. She pasted the same number of stamps on each page of her stampbook. How many stamps did she paste on the first page?

_____

Name _____

70 **DAILY CUMULATIVE REVIEW**

Write the money amount. Use a dollar sign and decimal point.

1. four dollars and fifty–eight cents _____

2. 6 dollars and 80 cents _____

3. three dollars and forty–five cents _____

4. 12 dollars and 72 cents _____

Solve each problem. You can use guess and check to help you.

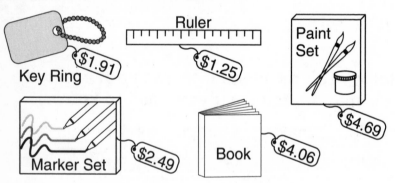

Ruler

Key Ring $1.91 $1.25

Paint Set

$4.69

Marker Set $2.49   Book $4.06

5. Misha bought 3 items. He spent $5.65. Which items did he buy?

_____

6. Juan bought 3 items. He spent $10. Which items did Juan buy?

_____

Name _____

71 **DAILY CUMULATIVE REVIEW**

Write the missing numbers.

1. 75, 76, 77, _____, _____, _____, _____, _____

2. 97, _____, _____, _____, _____, _____, 103

3. 448, _____, 450, _____, 452, _____, _____

4. 525, 524, _____, 522, _____, _____, _____

Write the answer.

5. $\begin{array}{r} 58 \\ 79 \\ +\ 12 \\ \hline \end{array}$ **6.** $\begin{array}{r} 505 \\ 28 \\ +\ 626 \\ \hline \end{array}$ **7.** $\begin{array}{r} 80 \\ 147 \\ +\ 98 \\ \hline \end{array}$

8. $\begin{array}{r} 430 \\ -\ 275 \\ \hline \end{array}$ **9.** $\begin{array}{r} 965 \\ -\ 488 \\ \hline \end{array}$ **10.** $\begin{array}{r} 532 \\ -\ 105 \\ \hline \end{array}$

Solve.

11. Levin bought 4 cans of juice. Each can fills 4 cups. How many cups can Levin fill?   _____

72 DAILY CUMULATIVE REVIEW

Order from least to greatest.

1. 785, 777, 770, 877 _____

2. 506, 660, 606, 560 _____

3. 7095, 7905, 7590 _____

Write the time.

4.

5.

6.

_____   _____   _____

Solve each problem.

7. Marco paid for a book with two dollar bills. His change was $0.31. How much did Marco spend? _____

8. Karen paid for her lunch with three dollar bills. She received $0.45 in change. How much did Karen's lunch cost? _____

DAILY CUMULATIVE REVIEW

Write the number in standard form.

1. five hundred eighty   _____

2. three thousand four hundred   _____

3. two thousand nine hundred fifty-four   _____

4. six thousand fifty   _____

Complete the number sentence.

5. $9 + \underline{\hspace{1cm}} = 16$ **6.** $\underline{\hspace{1cm}} + 8 = 13$

7. $\underline{\hspace{1cm}} + 8 = 15$ **8.** $18 = 9 + \underline{\hspace{1cm}}$

9. $17 = \underline{\hspace{1cm}} + 9$ **10.** $5 + \underline{\hspace{1cm}} = 14$

Use the table to answer each question.

11. How many more points did Heather score than Pierre?

_____

12. How many more points would Cassie need to tie Omar's score?

Game Scores	
Player	**Points**
Pierre	86
Heather	110
Omar	124
Cassie	98

_____

Name _____

Write the answer.

1.   86
   + 53
   _____

2.   95
   + 290
   _____

3. $2.48
   + 4.87
   _____

4.   90
   − 45
   _____

5.   688
   − 79
   _____

6. $5.60
   − 2.85
   _____

7. 423 + 84 + 302 + 150 = _____

Use the map to answer each question.

8. Hilda walked from The Castle to Rocky Road to the Animal Kingdom. How far did she walk?

   _____

9. Nathan started at the place closest to the Snack Stand. Where did Nathan start?

   _____

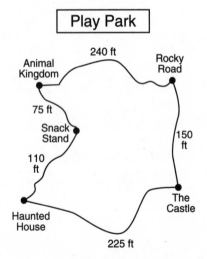

Name _____

Write the product.

1.	2.	3.	4.
2 × 1	4 × 2	2 × 5	3 × 2

5.	6.	7.	8.
3 × 3	3 × 4	5 × 3	1 × 3

9.	10.	11.	12.
4 × 1	5 × 4	2 × 4	4 × 3

Estimate. Write *yes* or *no*.

13. Did Adam sell at least 600 Space Things and Ice Creatures?

_____

14. Did Adam sell more than 800 Robot Boys and Action Girls?

_____

Adam's Action Figure Sales	
Action Figure	**Number Sold**
Robot Boy	428
Action Girl	337
Space Thing	249
Ice Creature	380
Plastic Man	200

76 DAILY CUMULATIVE REVIEW

Write the quotient.

1. $4 \div 2 =$ _____   **2.** $8 \div 2 =$ _____

3. $25 \div 5 =$ _____   **4.** $9 \div 3 =$ _____

5. $12 \div 3 =$ _____   **6.** $6 \div 2 =$ _____

7. $12 \div 4 =$ _____   **8.** $16 \div 4 =$ _____

Use the pattern to complete the table.
Use the table to solve each problem.

9.

Kim's Stamp Book					
Page	1	2	3		
Number of Stamps	4	8			

10. How many stamps does Kim put on each page?

11. How many stamps will Kim have on 4 pages?

_____   _____

12. How many pages will Kim need for 20 stamps?

_____

Name _____

 77 DAILY CUMULATIVE REVIEW

Write the value of the digit 4.

1. 405 _____   **2.** 4350 _____

3. 7604 _____   **4.** 49 _____

Write the digit that is in the hundreds place.

5. 4619 _____   **6.** 378 _____

7. 590 _____   **8.** 4930 _____

Complete the fact family.

9. $3 \times$ _____ $= 6$ **10.** _____ $\times 3 = 12$

$2 \times 3 =$ _____ $3 \times 4 =$ _____

$6 \div$ _____ $= 2$ $12 \div 4 =$ _____

_____ $\div 2 = 3$ $12 \div$ _____ $= 4$

Solve.

11. Alberto arranged the chairs for the class play. He put 5 chairs in each row. How many chairs are there in 4 rows? _____

78 DAILY CUMULATIVE REVIEW

Complete the table. Use counters if you like.

1.

Total number of counters	Number of equal sets	How many in each set?
25	5	
16	4	
15	3	
20	5	
9	3	

Write the product.

2. 2
 × 4

3. 4
 × 3

4. 1
 × 2

5. 3
 × 3

6. 5
 × 2

7. 4
 × 1

8. 5
 × 3

9. 2
 × 3

Solve.

10. Each picture frame holds 2 pictures. How many frames are needed for 10 pictures? _____

79 ▸ DAILY CUMULATIVE REVIEW

Write the correct change.

1. $1.00 paid for a pad that cost 69¢. _____

2. $1.50 paid for a pen that cost $1.29. _____

Write an addition sentence and a multiplication sentence for each set.

3. ✳ ✳ ✳ ✳ ✳
   ✳ ✳ ✳ ✳ ✳
   ✳ ✳ ✳ ✳ ✳

4. ✳ ✳ ✳ ✳
   ✳ ✳ ✳ ✳
   ✳ ✳ ✳ ✳
   ✳ ✳ ✳ ✳

_____

_____

_____

_____

5. ✳ ✳ ✳ ✳
   ✳ ✳ ✳ ✳
   ✳ ✳ ✳ ✳

6. ✳ ✳ ✳
   ✳ ✳ ✳

_____

_____

_____

_____

Solve.

7. There are 9 innings in a baseball game. How many innings will there be if the teams play 2 games? _____

Name _____

....

Use the correct bar graph to answer each question.

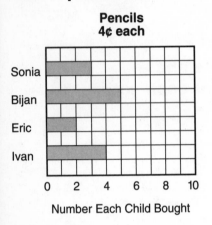

Pencils
4¢ each

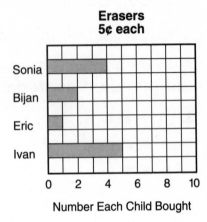

Erasers
5¢ each

1. Which student bought
   5 pencils? _____

2. How much money did Sonia
   spend for pencils? _____

3. How many more erasers did
   Sonia buy than Eric? _____

4. How much money did Ivan
   spend for erasers? _____

5. Sonia paid for her erasers
   with a quarter. What was her
   change? _____

6. What was the total amount
   Bijan spent for pencils and
   erasers? _____

81 ▸ DAILY CUMULATIVE REVIEW

Count by 5's. Write the numbers.

1. 200, 205, 210, _____ , _____ , _____ , _____

2. 145, 140, _____ , _____ , _____ , _____ , 115

Count by 2's. Write the numbers.

3. 76, 78, _____ , _____ , _____ , _____ , _____

4. 52, 50, 48, _____ , 44, _____ , _____ , _____

Write the answer. Use mental math.

5.	**6.**	**7.**	**8.**
2	12	7	17
+ 10	+ 10	+ 1	+ 1

9.	**10.**	**11.**	**12.**
6	16	5	15
+ 1	+ 1	+ 10	+ 10

Solve. Write A.M. or P.M. in your answer.

13. The moving truck arrived at the Marconi's house at 9:30 A.M. It took 4 hours to load the furniture. What time was the truck ready to leave?

_____

82 DAILY CUMULATIVE REVIEW

Test the multiplication properties. Find the products. Use a calculator for the larger numbers.

1. 3 × 2 = _____

2 × 3 = _____

2. 5 × 3 = _____

3 × 5 = _____

3. 0 × 8 = _____

8 × 0 = _____

4. 4 × 5 = _____

5 × 4 = _____

5. 20 × 10 = _____

10 × 20 = _____

6. 45 × 4 = _____

4 × 45 = _____

Solve. You can use guess and check.

7. Myron spent 21¢ for Fruit Bars and Raisin Logs. How many of each did he buy?

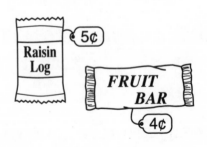

_____

_____

8. If you multiply this mystery number by itself and then add 10, you get 35. What is the mystery number?

_____

DAILY CUMULATIVE REVIEW

Write the time.

1.

2.

3.

_____   _____   _____

4.

5.

6.

_____   _____   _____

Write the missing factor.

7. _____ × 5 = 25   **8.** 2 × _____ = 2

9. 2 × _____ = 12   **10.** _____ × 4 = 12

11. 4 × _____ = 8   **12.** _____ × 3 = 15

13. _____ × 5 = 20   **14.** 3 × _____ = 9

Solve.

15. Each basket has 4 tomatoes.
How many tomatoes will Jan
have if she buys 5 baskets?   _____

84 DAILY CUMULATIVE REVIEW

Make a rough front-end estimate. Then adjust.

1.   246
   + 389

2.   378
   + 389

3. $4.12
   + 4.75

4.   340
     298
   + 79

5.   190
     306
   + 511

6. $6.68
     1.12
   + 1.85

Solve each problem. If there is not enough information, tell what you need to know.

7. Ms. Jackson is driving round trip from Philadelphia to Boston. The trip is 296 miles one way. How far will she drive both ways?

_____

8. Ms. Jackson will stay in a hotel in Boston for 2 nights. What will be the total cost for the hotel?

_____

85 DAILY CUMULATIVE REVIEW

Complete the fact family.

1. $6 \times 3 =$ _____

$3 \times 6 =$ _____

$18 \div 3 =$ _____

$18 \div 6 =$ _____

2. $5 \times 6 =$ _____

$6 \times 5 =$ _____

$30 \div 6 =$ _____

$30 \div 5 =$ _____

3. $4 \times 6 = 24$

_____

$24 \div 4 = 6$

_____

4. $5 \times 4 = 20$

_____

$20 \div 4 = 5$

_____

Write the money amount. Use a dollar sign and decimal point.

5. ten dollars and thirty-five cents _____

6. six dollars and seventy cents _____

7. 14 dollars and 95 cents _____

Estimate. Then add.

8. How much money would you need to buy a ring for $6.29 and a pin for $2.36?

_____

86 DAILY CUMULATIVE REVIEW

Write the number the arrow is pointing to.

1.

55 ■ 61

_____

2.

■ 79 80

_____

3.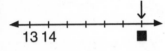

13 14 ■

_____

4.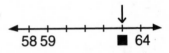

58 59 ■ 64

_____

Fill in the multiplication table.

5.

×	1	2	3	4	5
1					
2					
3					
4					
5					

Solve.

6. Tickets to the aquarium cost
$4 for each child. What will
be the cost for 5 children?

_____

Name _____

··

Write the product.

1. $6 \times 2 =$ _____

$2 \times 6 =$ _____

2. $6 \times 7 =$ _____

$7 \times 6 =$ _____

3. $6 \times 4 =$ _____

$4 \times 6 =$ _____

4. $6 \times 8 =$ _____

$8 \times 6 =$ _____

5. $7 \times 5 =$ _____

$5 \times 7 =$ _____

6. $7 \times 8 =$ _____

$8 \times 7 =$ _____

Write the quotient.

7. $5\overline{)25}$

8. $6\overline{)30}$

9. $5\overline{)15}$

10. $4\overline{)12}$

11. $6\overline{)36}$

12. $7\overline{)49}$

Make a plan. Use it to solve the problem.

13. Marco has 12 baseball cards
in his collection. Today he
bought four more packs of
cards. Each pack has 6 cards.
How many baseball cards
does Marco have now? _____

88 DAILY CUMULATIVE REVIEW

Write the time.

1.

2.

3.

_____   _____   _____

Predict each product. Use the patterns to help you. Use place-value blocks to check your predictions.

4. $3 \times 5 =$ _____

$3 \times 50 =$ _____

$3 \times 500 =$ _____

5. $4 \times 3 =$ _____

$4 \times 30 =$ _____

$4 \times 300 =$ _____

6. $5 \times 2 =$ _____

$5 \times 20 =$ _____

$5 \times 200 =$ _____

7. $6 \times 8 =$ _____

$6 \times 80 =$ _____

$6 \times 800 =$ _____

Solve. Use the multiplication patterns to help you.

8. Each of 50 girls at Moppet's Camp earned 3 badges. How many badges are needed?

_____

Write the product.

1. $2 \times 8 =$ _____
   $8 \times 2 =$ _____

2. $8 \times 4 =$ _____
   $4 \times 8 =$ _____

3. $5 \times 8 =$ _____
   $8 \times 5 =$ _____

4. $1 \times 8 =$ _____
   $8 \times 1 =$ _____

5. $9 \times 3 =$ _____
   $3 \times 9 =$ _____

6. $4 \times 9 =$ _____
   $9 \times 4 =$ _____

Write the quotient.

7. $8\overline{)16}$

8. $3\overline{)24}$

9. $8\overline{)8}$

10. $9\overline{)45}$

11. $6\overline{)54}$

12. $9\overline{)27}$

Solve.

13. The Snack Shop puts 8 peanuts in each Mixed Nuts Pack it sells. How many peanuts will be needed for 6 Mixed Nuts Packs?

_____

90 **DAILY CUMULATIVE REVIEW**

Write > or <.

1. $5.25 $\bigcirc$ $2.55   2. 945 $\bigcirc$ 1045

3. 895 $\bigcirc$ 890   4. $7.12 $\bigcirc$ $7.75

5. 1054 $\bigcirc$ 1045   6. 998 $\bigcirc$ 1010

Predict each quotient. Use the patterns to help you. Use place-value blocks to check your predictions.

7. $18 \div 3 =$ _____   8. $9 \div 1 =$ _____

$180 \div 3 =$ _____ $90 \div 1 =$ _____

$1800 \div 3 =$ _____ $900 \div 1 =$ _____

9. $15 \div 5 =$ _____   10. $20 \div 4 =$ _____

$150 \div 5 =$ _____ $200 \div 4 =$ _____

$1500 \div 5 =$ _____ $2000 \div 4 =$ _____

Solve. Use the division patterns.

11. There are 60 people at a picnic. If 180 burgers are cooked, how many could each person eat?

_____

DAILY CUMULATIVE REVIEW

Write *slide* or *flip* for the set of figures.

1. 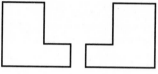   **2.**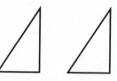

___   ___

Write the answer.

3. 728
   + 195

4. 450
   + 72

5. $3.88
   + 2.35

6. 615
   − 278

7. 720
   − 390

8. $5.45
   − 0.89

Solve.

9. Kevin spent $1.45.
Which two items
did he buy?

___

___

Yogurt — 70¢
apple — 35¢
Granola Pack — 75¢
Chocolate Milk — 40¢

92 ▸ DAILY CUMULATIVE REVIEW

Write the product.

1.	2.	3.	4.
11 × 2	11 × 3	12 × 2	12 × 3

5.	6.	7.	8.
11 × 7	12 × 4	12 × 5	11 × 8

Write the number of square corners for each figure.

9.

_____ square corners

10.

_____ square corners

11.

_____ square corners

12.

_____ square corners

Solve.

13. Draw a figure that has fewer square corners than a square.

93 DAILY CUMULATIVE REVIEW

Write the missing factor.

1. $5 \times$ _____ $= 25$ **2.** _____ $\times 4 = 32$

3. _____ $\times 3 = 21$ **4.** $4 \times$ _____ $= 20$

5. $9 \times$ _____ $= 18$ **6.** _____ $\times 8 = 24$

7. $4 \times$ _____ $= 16$ **8.** $7 \times$ _____ $= 35$

Write *yes* or *no* to tell if the dotted line is a line of symmetry.

9. 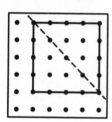   **10.**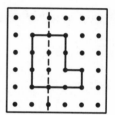

_____   _____

Write a division sentence. Draw a picture if you like.

11. 16 stickers shared equally between 2 girls   **12.** 25 pennies separated into sets of 5

_____   _____

Name _____

94 **DAILY CUMULATIVE REVIEW** ....

Write an addition sentence and a multiplication sentence for each set.

1. ✳ ✳ ✳ ✳ ✳ ✳
✳ ✳ ✳ ✳ ✳ ✳
✳ ✳ ✳ ✳ ✳ ✳

2. ✳ ✳ ✳ ✳ ✳ ✳ ✳
✳ ✳ ✳ ✳ ✳ ✳ ✳
✳ ✳ ✳ ✳ ✳ ✳ ✳
✳ ✳ ✳ ✳ ✳ ✳ ✳

_____

_____

_____

_____

Write the answer. Watch the signs.

3. $5 + 9 =$ _____

4. $8 \times 2 =$ _____

5. $14 - 8 =$ _____

6. $18 \div 2 =$ _____

7. $9 + 7 =$ _____

8. $5 \times 5 =$ _____

Finish the diagram to help solve the problem.

9. Julio was in line behind Kay. Lin was in front of Alona and behind Julio. What was the order of the children standing in line?

Julio

_____

Name _____

••

Write the answer. Watch the signs.

1. $6 \times 5 =$ _____

2. $7 + 5 =$ _____

3. $4 \times 9 =$ _____

4. $28 \div 7 =$ _____

5. $16 - 8 =$ _____

6. $5 \times 7 =$ _____

7. $7 + 8 =$ _____

8. $30 \div 6 =$ _____

Use the angles to answer the questions.

a.   **b.** 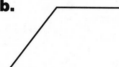   **c.**

d.   **e.**   **f.**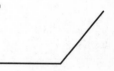

9. Which angles are less than a square corner?

10. Which angles are greater than a square corner?

11. Which angles are square corners? _____

96 ▸ DAILY CUMULATIVE REVIEW

Write the money amount. Use a dollar sign and decimal point.

1.   _____

2.   _____

Write a division sentence.

3. 30 counters
5 in each set
? sets

_____

4. 45 counters
9 in each set
? sets

_____

5. 24 counters
8 in each set
? sets

_____

6. 42 counters
6 in each set
? sets

_____

Solve.

7. At a book sale, Jean Marie
bought 6 mystery books for
5¢ each and 3 joke books for
10¢ each. How much money
did she spend?   _____

Name _____

Use the graph to solve each problem.

Scott sold tickets to the school fair. The graph shows how many tickets he sold each day.

1. How many tickets did Scott sell on Wednesday?

_____

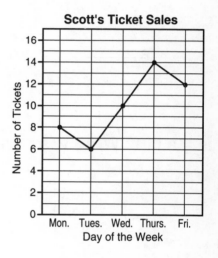

Scott's Ticket Sales

2. On which day did Scott sell the most tickets?

_____

3. On which day did Scott sell the fewest tickets?

_____

4. How many more tickets did Scott sell on Friday than on Monday?

_____

5. How many days did Scott sell more than 10 tickets?

_____

6. If each ticket costs 10¢, how much money did Scott collect on Wednesday?

_____

Write the answer.

1. 57
   + 82

2. 706
   − 75

3. $3.00
   − 2.50

4. 957
   + 67

5. 89
   − 80

6. $5.98
   + 2.12

Is it a flip? Write *yes* or *no*.

7.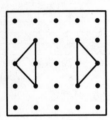

8.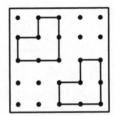

_____   _____

Use the spinner to answer the questions.

9. Which letter are you most
   likely to land on? _____

10. Are you more likely to
   land on B or Y? _____

99 ▸ DAILY CUMULATIVE REVIEW

Write the answer. Watch the signs.

1. $14 - 7 =$ _____   **2.** $9 \times 6 =$ _____

3. $6 + 2 =$ _____   **4.** $10 - 5 =$ _____

5. $21 \div 7 =$ _____   **6.** $6 + 9 =$ _____

7. $5 \times 5 =$ _____   **8.** $12 \div 4 =$ _____

Use the grid to answer each question.

9. Where is the heart?

_____

10. Where is the
happy face?

_____

11. Where is the flag?

_____

12. What is in A4?   **13.** What is in C3?

_____   _____

Name _____

Write *line*, *line segment*, or *neither* for each figure.

1.

_____

2.

_____

3.

_____

4.

_____

Draw a picture to help you solve each problem.

5. Billy began his art project on Tuesday, May third. He finished it 8 days later. What day and date was that?

MAY						
Sun.	Mon.	Tues.	Wed.	Thurs.	Fri.	Sat.
		3				

_____

6. Roshanda wants to cut a string into 6 pieces. How many cuts will she make in the string?

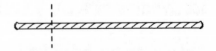

_____

Name _____

Write the sum.

1. 675 + 82	**2.** 921 + 304	**3.** $2.12 + 1.78

4. 203 592 + 75	**5.** $3.75 4.27 + 0.99	**6.** 627 236 + 189

Has the store clerk given the correct change? Write *too much*, *too little*, or *correct*.

7. Jay paid $1.50.

_____

8. Megan paid $2.00.

_____

9. Jordan paid $1.00.

_____

102 DAILY CUMULATIVE REVIEW

Write the missing numbers.

1. 675, _____, 677, _____, _____, _____, 681

2. _____, 897, _____, 899, _____, _____, 902

3. 997, 998, _____, _____, _____, _____, 1003

Use the pictograph to solve each problem.

Attendance at the Science Fair	
Monday	☺ ☺ ☺ ☺
Tuesday	☺ ☺
Wednesday	☺ ☺ ☺
Thursday	☺ ☺ ☺ ☺ ☺
Friday	☺ ☺ ☺ ☺ ☺ ☺

Key: ☺ = 10 people

4. On which day did the greatest number of people attend the science fair?

_____

5. How many people came to the science fair on Monday?

_____

6. How many more people attended on Thursday than on Tuesday?

_____

103 DAILY CUMULATIVE REVIEW

Write the money amount. Use a dollar sign and decimal point.

1. fifteen dollars and thirty-five cents _____

2. four dollars and fifty-two cents _____

3. twelve dollars and eighty cents _____

4. 25 dollars and 7 cents _____

5. 9 dollars and 99 cents _____

Complete each fact family.

6. $5 \times 3 = 15$ **7.** $4 \times 5 = 20$

_____   _____

$15 \div 3 = 5$ $20 \div 5 = 4$

_____   _____

Solve each problem.

8. Anna buys 4 eggs at 4¢ each. How much money does she spend?

_____

9. Jamal sells 5 cups of juice at 5¢ each. How much money does he earn?

_____

Name _____

104 **DAILY CUMULATIVE REVIEW**

Write two division sentences that belong to the same fact family.

1. $6 \times 7 = 42$ **2.** $8 \times 5 = 40$

_____   _____

_____   _____

3. $9 \times 5 = 45$ **4.** $4 \times 8 = 32$

_____   _____

_____   _____

Write the number of squares in each figure.

5.

6.

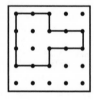

_____ squares   _____ squares

Solve.

7. Marissa is setting up tables for a picnic. She can fit 8 chairs at each table. How many tables will she need for 32 people?

_____

Name _____

105 DAILY CUMULATIVE REVIEW

Write > or <.

1. 614 ◯ 641

2. 875 ◯ 857

3. 412 ◯ 441

4. 999 ◯ 1001

5. 208 ◯ 802

6. 440 ◯ 404

Tell whether or not the line segments are parallel. Write *parallel* or *not parallel*.

7.

8.

_____

_____

9.

10.

_____

_____

Solve.

11. What is Charlie's number? It is an odd number between 270 and 280. If you add its digits together, the sum is 18.

_____

106 DAILY CUMULATIVE REVIEW

Write the answer. Use mental math.

1. 60 + 70 = _____   **2.** 80 + 90 = _____

3. 120 – 50 = _____   **4.** 180 – 50 = _____

5. 400 + 600 = _____   **6.** 1400 – 800 = _____

7. 2000 – 600 = _____   **8.** 300 + 900 = _____

Match each net with the correct solid figure.

9.

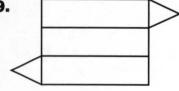 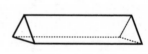

10.

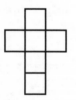

11.

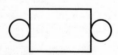

DAILY CUMULATIVE REVIEW

Use the patterns to find each product.

1. $3 \times 3 =$ _____   **2.** $4 \times 6 =$ _____

$3 \times 30 =$ _____ $4 \times 60 =$ _____

$3 \times 300 =$ _____ $4 \times 600 =$ _____

3. $6 \times 7 =$ _____   **4.** $5 \times 8 =$ _____

$6 \times 70 =$ _____ $5 \times 80 =$ _____

$6 \times 700 =$ _____ $5 \times 800 =$ _____

Write a fraction for the shaded part. Then write a fraction for the unshaded part.

5. 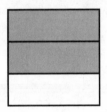   **6.** 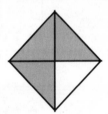   **7.**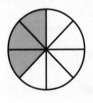

_____   _____   _____

Solve.

8. Morgan cut an apple into 4 parts. She ate 3 parts. How many parts are left?   _____

108 DAILY CUMULATIVE REVIEW

Write the answer.

1. $\begin{array}{r} 5 \\ \times 6 \\ \hline \end{array}$
2. $\begin{array}{r} 7 \\ \times 5 \\ \hline \end{array}$
3. $\begin{array}{r} 6 \\ \times 4 \\ \hline \end{array}$
4. $\begin{array}{r} 8 \\ \times 3 \\ \hline \end{array}$

5. $6\overline{)36}$ **6.** $4\overline{)32}$ **7.** $7\overline{)56}$

8. $4\overline{)24}$ **9.** $5\overline{)25}$ **10.** $6\overline{)54}$

Use the grid to answer each question.

11. Where is the park?

_____

12. Where is the school?

_____

13. What is at E1?

_____

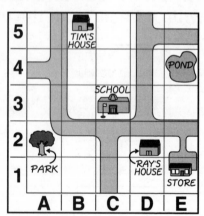

14. What is at B5?   **15.** What is at E4?

_____   _____

109 DAILY CUMULATIVE REVIEW

Write the value of the digit 5.

1. 256 _____

2. 590 _____

3. 385 _____

4. 9054 _____

5. 5890 _____

6. 6085 _____

Estimate. About what fraction of the bread is left? Write $\frac{1}{4}$, $\frac{1}{2}$, or $\frac{3}{4}$.

7.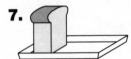

8.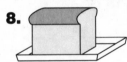

9.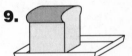

_____

Solve each problem.

10. Alfredo left school at 3:15 and arrived home $\frac{3}{4}$ of an hour later. What time did Alfredo arrive home?

_____

11. Teri practiced the piano for $\frac{1}{2}$ hour. She began at 3:45. What time did Teri finish practicing the piano?

_____

Name _____

Use Fraction Bars to compare each pair
of fractions. Write > or < or =.

1. $\frac{1}{2}$ ◯ $\frac{1}{3}$ **2.** $\frac{1}{4}$ ◯ $\frac{1}{3}$ **3.** $\frac{2}{4}$ ◯ $\frac{1}{2}$

4. $\frac{2}{3}$ ◯ $\frac{2}{5}$ **5.** $\frac{1}{3}$ ◯ $\frac{2}{6}$ **6.** $\frac{2}{5}$ ◯ $\frac{4}{5}$

7. $\frac{1}{6}$ ◯ $\frac{1}{4}$ **8.** $\frac{1}{3}$ ◯ $\frac{2}{5}$ **9.** $\frac{2}{8}$ ◯ $\frac{1}{4}$

Write the fraction of an hour that has
passed. Write $\frac{1}{4}$, $\frac{1}{2}$, or $\frac{3}{4}$.

10. 3:00 to 3:30   **11.** 4:00 to 4:15

_____   _____

12. 11:15 to 12:00   **13.** 6:15 to 6:30

_____   _____

Solve. Use the diagram if it helps.

14. Cecil bought
12 tiles to cover
his bathroom floor.
Half of the tiles are
white. How many
are white?

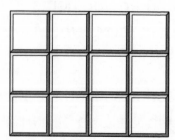

_____

Name _____

Write the answer.

1. 9
    × 6

2. 8
    × 1

3. 9
    × 5

4. 6
    × 7

5. 8)48   **6.** 2)18   **7.** 7)49

Write a mixed number for the shaded part.

8.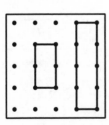

9.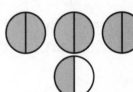

_____   _____

Are the figures the same shape and size? Write *yes* or *no*.

10.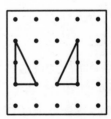

11.

_____   _____

112 **DAILY CUMULATIVE REVIEW**

Write the answer.

1. 258
+ 379

2. 712
+ 218

3. $4.90
+ 2.78

4. 450
− 212

5. 579
− 85

6. $8.06
− 1.60

Write a fraction for the shaded part.
Write a fraction for the unshaded part.

7.

8.

_____   _____

Solve.

| 45 | 65 | 88 | 71 | 96 | 80 |

9. Owen scores a total of
264 points on 3 math tests.
Choose 3 numbers from the
box that could be his test
scores. _____

DAILY CUMULATIVE REVIEW

Fill in the multiplication table.

1.

×	5	6	7	8	9
5					
6					
7					
8					
9					

Write the number of square corners each figure has.

2.

_____ square corners

3.

_____ square corners

Solve.

4. Draw a triangle that has 1 square corner.

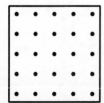

5. Draw a figure that has 2 square corners.

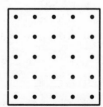

Name _____

Write the answer. Watch the signs.

1. $9 \times 6 =$ _____   **2.** $8 + 6 =$ _____

3. $32 \div 4 =$ _____   **4.** $17 - 8 =$ _____

5. $6 \times 6 =$ _____   **6.** $45 \div 9 =$ _____

7. $9 + 9 =$ _____   **8.** $8 \times 7 =$ _____

9. $21 \div 3 =$ _____   **10.** $15 - 7 =$ _____

Write the time. Use *quarter past*, *half past*, or *quarter to*.

11.

_____

12.

_____

13.

_____

14.

_____

Name _____

Write the answer.

1. 7 × 5	**2.** 8 × 7	**3.** 5 × 9	**4.** 6 × 8

5. 8)64   **6.** 5)30   **7.** 8)56

8. 3)24   **9.** 7)28   **10.** 9)72

Draw a line of symmetry for each figure.

11. 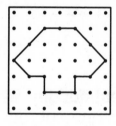   **12.**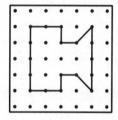

Solve the problem.

13. Layla rode her bike for $\frac{1}{4}$ hour. Deanna road her bike from 3:15 to 3:45. Who rode her bike longer?

_____

....

Complete each number sentence.

1. _____ × 6 = 30   **2.** 8 × _____ = 48

   6 × 5 = _____   6 × 8 = _____

   30 ÷ _____ = 5   48 ÷ _____ = 6

   _____ ÷ 5 = 6   _____ ÷ 6 = 8

Order from least to greatest.

3. 760, 902, 845, 706   _____

4. 990, 1090, 1009   _____

5. 4029, 2049, 2409   _____

Solve each problem.

6. Every Saturday Michele mows 10 lawns. She has already mowed 7 lawns. How many more lawns does she have to mow?

7. Lamont bought 4 packages of red pencils. There are 8 red pencils in each package. How many red pencils did he buy?

_____   _____

117 DAILY CUMULATIVE REVIEW

Use the number line. Round each number to the nearest ten.

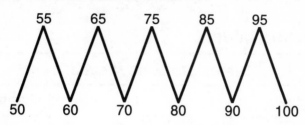

1. 56 _____   **2.** 68 _____

3. 62 _____   **4.** 75 _____

5. 81 _____   **6.** 98 _____

Write >, <, or =. Use Fraction Bars to help you.

7. $\frac{3}{4}$ ◯ $\frac{2}{3}$ **8.** $\frac{3}{7}$ ◯ $\frac{2}{7}$ **9.** $\frac{7}{10}$ ◯ $\frac{9}{10}$

10. $\frac{2}{4}$ ◯ $\frac{3}{4}$ **11.** $\frac{1}{3}$ ◯ $\frac{2}{6}$ **12.** $\frac{5}{8}$ ◯ $\frac{5}{8}$

Solve the problem.

13. Sergei writes a number that is greater than 5006 and less than 5010. What numbers could it be?

_____

Name _____

 DAILY CUMULATIVE REVIEW ....

Mr. Kent's class made a table to show which states the students have visited.

Complete the table.

1.

States Students Visited		
State	**Tally**	**Number**
West Virginia	~~||||~~ ~~||||~~ ||	
Virginia	||||	
North Carolina	~~||||~~ ~~||||~~ ||||	
Kentucky	~~||||~~ |||	
Delaware	|	
Maryland	~~||||~~ |	

Use the table to answer each question.

2. How many students have
   visited Maryland?   _____

3. Which state have the fewest
   students visited?   _____

4. How many more students
   have visited West Virginia
   than Virginia?   _____

119 DAILY CUMULATIVE REVIEW

Circle the letter of the closest estimate.

1.	**2.**	**3.**
980	485	$6.32
− 325	− 290	− 1.86

a. 200	**a.** 200	**a.** $5
b. 400	**b.** 400	**b.** $6
c. 600	**c.** 700	**c.** $7

Test the multiplication properties. Find the products. Use a calculator for the larger numbers.

4. $1 \times 52 =$ _____   **5.** $0 \times 12 =$ _____

$52 \times 1 =$ _____ $12 \times 0 =$ _____

6. $5 \times 10 =$ _____   **7.** $12 \times 5 =$ _____

$10 \times 5 =$ _____ $5 \times 12 =$ _____

Estimate. About how full is the glass? Write $\frac{1}{4}$, $\frac{1}{2}$, or $\frac{3}{4}$.

8.   **9.**   **10.**

_____   _____   _____

Name _____

Write the sum or difference. Use Fraction Bars to help you.

1. $\frac{2}{4} + \frac{1}{4} =$ _____

2. $\frac{2}{6} + \frac{2}{6} =$ _____

3. $\frac{1}{3} + \frac{1}{3} =$ _____

4. $\frac{2}{5} + \frac{1}{5} =$ _____

5. $\frac{4}{8} - \frac{2}{8} =$ _____

6. $\frac{2}{3} - \frac{1}{3} =$ _____

7. $\frac{7}{8} - \frac{2}{8} =$ _____

8. $\frac{5}{6} - \frac{2}{6} =$ _____

Write the number of cubes in each figure.

9.   10.   11.

_____   _____   _____

Solve.

12. Mrs. Weiss had $315 in the bank. In the morning she puts in $25. In the afternoon she takes out $75. How much money does she have in the bank now?

_____

121 DAILY CUMULATIVE REVIEW

Draw another figure that has the same shape and size. Follow the direction.

1. Draw a flip image.

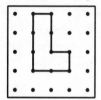 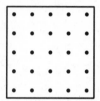

2. Draw a half turn image.

 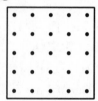

Solve. If there is not enough information, tell what you need to know.

3. At the track meet, 8 runners enter the 100-meter race. Twice as many runners enter the 200–meter race. How many runners are in the 200–meter race?

_____

4. Marc entered 3 racing events, 5 jumping events, and some swimming events. How many events did he enter altogether?

_____

122 DAILY CUMULATIVE REVIEW

Predict the quotient. Then use a calculator to check your prediction.

1. $18 \div 1 =$ _____

2. $56 \div 56 =$ _____

3. $0 \div 20 =$ _____

4. $235 \div 1 =$ _____

5. $0 \div 14 =$ _____

6. $142 \div 142 =$ _____

Solve each problem. Use one of the strategies you have learned.

7. Ms. Klein's class is painting a mural for the school play. They painted from 10:00 to 11:30. How many hours is that? _____

8. Each roll of mural paper costs $3.50. Ms. Klein has $6. Can she buy two more rolls of paper? _____

9. The can of red paint is $\frac{1}{2}$ full. The The can of green paint is $\frac{3}{4}$ full. Is there more red paint or more green paint? How do you know?

Red Paint

Green Paint

Name _____

 DAILY CUMULATIVE REVIEW ....

Write the answer.

1. 6
   × 8

2. 9
   × 3

3. 5
   × 2

4. 7
   × 0

5. 4
   × 5

6. 7
   × 3

7. 1
   × 8

8. 8
   × 9

9. $5\overline{)25}$

10. $6\overline{)30}$

11. $8\overline{)48}$

12. $9\overline{)81}$

13. $7\overline{)56}$

14. $4\overline{)32}$

Measure to the nearest half inch. Write the length.

15. ———————————   _____ in.

16. ——————   _____ in.

17. ————————————   _____ in.

Solve.

18. Jason is 4 feet tall. There
   are 12 inches in 1 foot. How
   tall is Jason in inches?   _____

Name _____

Write the correct change.

1. $1.50 paid for a puzzle that
cost $1.38   _____

2. $2.00 paid for toothpaste
that cost $1.57   _____

Write the answer. Watch the signs.

3. $6 + 9 =$ _____   **4.** $6 \times 7 =$ _____

5. $16 - 9 =$ _____   **6.** $8 + 6 =$ _____

7. $7 \times 7 =$ _____   **8.** $35 \div 5 =$ _____

Write the perimeter.

9.

2 in. | 10 in. | 2 in.
10 in.

10.

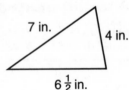

7 in.   4 in.

$6\frac{1}{2}$ in.

_____ **in.**   _____ **in.**

Solve. Draw a picture to help you.

11. Armond has a square flower
garden. Each side measures
4 feet. What is the distance
around his flower garden?   _____

Name _____

Which unit would you use to measure? Write *feet, yards,* or *miles.*

1. distance to another town _____

2. width of a refrigerator _____

3. length of the classroom _____

4. distance from your house
to school _____

Write the number the spinner is most likely to land on.

5.

6.

7.

_____   _____   _____

Solve.

8. Mark has $\frac{5}{6}$ of a pizza. He
gives $\frac{1}{6}$ of the pizza to his
sister and $\frac{1}{6}$ to his brother.
How much does Mark have left?

126 DAILY CUMULATIVE REVIEW

Write the fraction of an hour that has passed. Write $\frac{1}{4}$, $\frac{1}{2}$, or $\frac{3}{4}$.

1. 12:00 to 12:15   **2.** 11:00 to 11:30

_____   _____

3. 3:30 to 4:15   **4.** 6:15 to 6:30

_____   _____

Choose the better unit of measure. Write *a* or *b*.

5. glass of juice   _____
   a. cup   **b.** quart

6. can of paint   _____
   a. cup   **b.** gallon

7. can of soup   _____
   a. cup   **b.** quart

Solve each problem.

8. Marshall has 2 quarters. Can he buy 8 stickers for 5¢ each?

_____

9. Indira has $1.00. Can she buy 5 pinwheels for a quarter each?

_____

Name _____

Write a mixed number for the shaded part.

1. 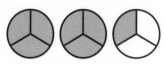 **2.**

_____   _____

Which unit would you use to measure?
Write *ounce* or *pound*.

3. a bunch of bananas   _____

4. one grape   _____

5. a small bird   _____

6. a horse   _____

Use the diagram to solve the problem.

7. Clark is putting a border around his design. Each rectangle is the same length as a square. How many more rectangles does he need?

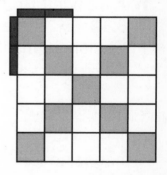

_____

DAILY CUMULATIVE REVIEW

Measure to the nearest centimeter. Write the length.

1. ━━━━━━━━━━━   _____ cm

2. ━━━━━━━━━━━━━━━   _____ cm

3. ━━━━━━━━━━   _____ cm

Choose the better estimate. Write *a* or *b*.

4. height of a one-story house   _____
   a. 10 m   **b.** 10 km

5. distance from Boston to New York   _____
   a. 306 cm **b.** 306 km

6. length of a book   _____
   a. 18 cm   **b.** 18 m

Solve each problem.

7. A train left Red Station at
   8:42 A.M. and arrived at Blue
   Station 15 minutes later.
   What time did the train arrive?   _____

8. Rachel read a book from
   5:15 to 5:45. Manny read a
   magazine for $\frac{3}{4}$ hour. Who
   spent more time reading?   _____

129 DAILY CUMULATIVE REVIEW

Write the time shown on the clock.

1.

2.

3.

_____   _____   _____

Write the answer.

4. $8\overline{)24}$ **5.** $9\overline{)45}$ **6.** $5\overline{)40}$

7. $9\overline{)63}$ **8.** $5\overline{)35}$ **9.** $6\overline{)42}$

10. $\begin{array}{r} 8 \\ \times\, 5 \\ \hline \end{array}$ **11.** $\begin{array}{r} 5 \\ \times\, 6 \\ \hline \end{array}$ **12.** $\begin{array}{r} 9 \\ \times\, 9 \\ \hline \end{array}$ **13.** $\begin{array}{r} 8 \\ \times\, 9 \\ \hline \end{array}$

Solve.

14. Kevin spent $5.65 to buy two items. Which two items did he buy?

Name _____

Write the answer. Use mental math when you can.

1.	675 + 188	2.	910 − 245	3.	$2.04 + 6.14

4.	600 − 258	5.	486 + 390	6.	$8.07 − 2.98

Choose the better estimate. Write *a* or *b*.

7. playing a baseball game _____
   a. 2 minutes **b.** 2 hours

8. brushing your teeth _____
   a. 1 second **b.** 1 minute

9. doing your homework _____
   a. 30 minutes **b.** 30 hours

Solve.

974 865 612 314 87 298

10. Leon found two numbers in the box that have a difference of 567. Which two numbers did Leon find? _____

DAILY CUMULATIVE REVIEW

Write the number of squares in each figure.

1.

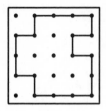

_____

2.

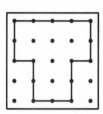

_____

Write the time. Use *quarter past*, *half past*, or *quarter to*.

3.

_____

4.

_____

Solve. Use a calculator or mental math.

5. Tim earns 50¢ for each dog he walks. If he walks 6 dogs, how much will he earn?

_____

6. Sy's mother buys hot dogs for $3.89, rolls for $1.45, and mustard for $0.89. How much does she spend?

_____

Write the answer.

1. 7
   × 6

2. 5
   × 7

3. 8
   × 3

4. 6
   × 9

5. 9)54

6. 7)49

7. 8)64

Count to estimate the number of squares in each.

8.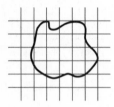

9.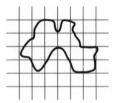

_____   _____

Use the table to solve the problem.

10. Darius works in the art room. If Darius works for 30 minutes, which chores can he get done?

Art Room Chores	
Clean brushes	10 min
Wipe tables	15 min
Put away clay	5 min
Sweep floor	10 min
Mix paint	20 min

_____

Name _____

 DAILY CUMULATIVE REVIEW

Use a ruler to draw the line segment.

1. 3 in.

2. $1\frac{1}{2}$ in.

Write a related division sentence.

3. $8 \times 5 = 40$ **4.** $9 \times 6 = 54$

_____   _____

Solve each problem. Make a plan to show your steps.

5. Zachary has $3.50. He buys a toy robot for $0.89 and a plastic turtle for $1.35. Does he have enough money left to buy a spaceship model for $1.29?

_____

6. Marika can make 4 clay bowls in an hour. If she works from 10:00 until 2:00, how many bowls will she make?

_____

Name _____

 DAILY CUMULATIVE REVIEW

Write the sum or difference. Use Fraction Bars to help you.

1. $\frac{4}{5} - \frac{1}{5} =$ _____

2. $\frac{7}{8} - \frac{4}{8} =$ _____

3. $\frac{5}{8} + \frac{1}{8} =$ _____

4. $\frac{1}{6} + \frac{1}{6} =$ _____

5. $\frac{3}{4} - \frac{2}{4} =$ _____

6. $\frac{4}{6} - \frac{1}{6} =$ _____

7. $\frac{3}{5} + \frac{1}{5} =$ _____

8. $\frac{2}{6} + \frac{3}{6} =$ _____

Write these measures in order from lightest to heaviest.

9. 3 pounds 12 ounces   _____

3 pounds 4 ounces   _____

2 pounds 14 ounces   _____

4 pounds 1 ounce   _____

Solve.

10. If Maurice spins this spinner ten times, which number do you think he will spin most often?

_____

Name _____

Which unit would you use? Write *milliliter* or *liter.*

1. mug _____

2. bucket _____

3. small bowl _____

4. small spoon _____

5. bathtub _____

Use the thermometer to answer the questions.

6. Which is colder, 20°F or 20°C?

_____

7. What Celsius temperature is about the same as 50°F?

_____

8. Which is warmer, 5°C or 30°F?

_____

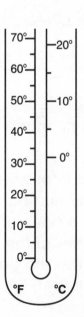

136 **DAILY CUMULATIVE REVIEW**

Write how much time has passed.

1. 7:15 to 7:30   **2.** 10:30 to 10:58

_____   _____

3. 6:02 to 6:20   **4.** 2:15 to 2:50

_____   _____

Write a fraction and a decimal for the shaded part.

5. 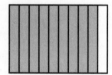   **6.**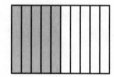

_____   _____

Solve the problem by completing the list.

7. Mysha knows her address has the numbers 5, 7, and 8. But she does not remember the order of the numbers. What are the possible ways the numbers could be arranged?

| 578 |
| 587 |

Name _____

Write >, <, or =.

1. 906 ◯ 960

2. 1210 ◯ 1201

3. 5 tens ◯ 50 ones

4. 9 hundreds ◯ 800

5. 4 tens ◯ 400

6. 618 ◯ 8 hundreds

Write the decimal.

7. 2 and 4 tenths

8. 6 tenths

_____

_____

9. eight tenths

10. $\frac{7}{10}$

_____

_____

Use the diagram to solve the problem.

11. Ms. Quinn wants to put a fence around her yard. If fencing is sold by the foot, how much fencing will she need?

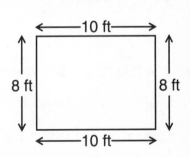

_____

DAILY CUMULATIVE REVIEW

Complete each fact family.

1. $7 \times 6 = 42$ **2.** $8 \times 9 = 72$

_____   _____

_____   _____

_____   _____

Write >, <, or =. Use the table to help you.

L	1	2	3	4	5
mL	1000	2000	3000	4000	5000

3. 4 L $\bigcirc$ 4000 mL   **4.** 500 mL $\bigcirc$ 5 L

5. 2 L $\bigcirc$ 200 mL   **6.** 3000 mL $\bigcirc$ 3 L

7. 400 mL $\bigcirc$ 4 L   **8.** 1 L $\bigcirc$ 100 mL

Write a fraction for each number.

9. Mariah has three tenths of a dollar.   _____

10. Leo rode two and five tenths miles.   _____

11. Alyssa has read nine tenths of a book. _____

12. Aldo walked 0.6 of a mile.   _____

DAILY CUMULATIVE REVIEW

Circle the letter of the closest estimate.

1.	890	**2.**	345	**3.**	800
	− 175		+ 265		− 295

1.	**2.**	**3.**
a. 700	**a.** 500	**a.** 350
b. 800	**b.** 600	**b.** 400
c. 900	**c.** 700	**c.** 600

Solve each problem. Use the calendar or the ad to help you.

June						
Sun.	Mon.	Tues.	Wed.	Thurs.	Fri.	Sat.
		1	2	3	4	5
6	7	8	9	10	11	12
13	14	15	16	17	18	19
20	21	22	23	24	25	26
27	28	29	30			

Boating Trip
on the River
June 27

Leaves at 9 A.M.
4 hour boat ride
$25.00 per person
Lunch included.

4. On June 6, Jervis reads an ad for a boating trip. In how many weeks will the boating trip start?

_____

5. Stella has a $10 bill, 8 quarters, and 5 dimes. How much more does she need for the boating trip?

_____

Name _____

140 DAILY CUMULATIVE REVIEW

**Which unit would you use? Write *gram*
or *kilogram*.**

1. banana   _____

2. horse   _____

3. pencil   _____

4. yourself   _____

**Write >, <, or =. Use tenths squares or
a number line if it helps.**

5. 1.8 ◯ 2   6. 3.5 ◯ 3.1

7. 7.0 ◯ 7   8. 4.0 ◯ 4.5

9. 1.9 ◯ 2.3   10. 2.2 ◯ 1.1

Solve the problem by completing the list.

11. Nathan buys
3 pair of shorts
and 2 shirts for
camp. His shorts
are tan, red, and
green. His shirts
are blue and white.
How many
different outfits
can Nathan make? _____

tan shorts, blue shirt
tan shorts, white shirt

Name _____

Write the sum.

1. $1 + 6 + 8 =$ _____   **2.** $5 + 9 + 5 =$ _____

3. $9 + 5 + 2 =$ _____   **4.** $7 + 5 + 8 =$ _____

Write the quotient.

5. $5\overline{)40}$ **6.** $8\overline{)32}$ **7.** $6\overline{)36}$

8. $8\overline{)56}$ **9.** $6\overline{)42}$ **10.** $9\overline{)81}$

Use the graph to answer the questions.

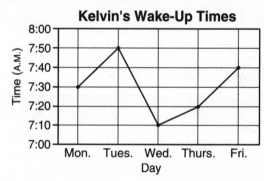

Kelvin's Wake-Up Times

11. On which morning did Kelvin wake up before 7:20 A.M.?

12. How much later did Kelvin sleep on Tuesday than on Friday?

_____   _____

Name _____

142 DAILY CUMULATIVE REVIEW

Write the time.

1. 　　**2.** 　　**3.**

_____　　_____　　_____

Write how much time has passed.

4. 9:05 A.M. to 9:20 A.M.　　_____

5. 6:15 P.M. to 6:34 P.M.　　_____

6. 8:12 P.M. to 8:17 P.M.　　_____

Solve. Make a list to help you.

7. Ali, Renata, and Curtis form a line to wait for their music lessons. How many different ways can they form the line?

Ali, Renata, Curtis
Ali, Curtis, Renata

_____

DAILY CUMULATIVE REVIEW

Write the decimal the arrow is pointing to.

1.

2.7 2.8 ■ 3.3

2.

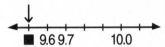

■ 9.6 9.7   10.0

_____   _____

Write the sum or difference. Use Fraction Bars to help you.

3. $\dfrac{5}{10} + \dfrac{2}{10} =$ _____

4. $\dfrac{5}{6} - \dfrac{1}{6} =$ _____

5. $\dfrac{3}{4} - \dfrac{2}{4} =$ _____

6. $\dfrac{3}{8} + \dfrac{3}{8} =$ _____

Solve each problem.

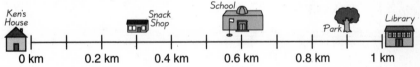

Ken's House · Snack Shop · School · Park · Library

0 km   0.2 km   0.4 km   0.6 km   0.8 km   1 km

7. Ken walks from his house to the library. He stops at the Snack Shop. How far has he walked? Is he halfway there?

_____

8. When Ken has walked 0.9 km, where is he?

_____

Name _____

Write the answer.

1. 6.4
     + 2.7

2. 0.7
     + 1.5

3. 4.2 cm
     − 2.8 cm

4. 9.0
     − 8.2

5. 4.5
     + 0.8

6. 2.3 m
     − 1.5 m

Which two numbers in the box have a product of:

7. about 90?

46   95
2   4

_____

8. about 200?

_____

9. about 400?

_____

Solve. Write whether you estimated or computed exactly.

10. Juan has $20. Is that enough money
    to buy a helmet for $11.99 and a
    hockey stick for $8.75?

_____

145 DAILY CUMULATIVE REVIEW

Use the patterns to find each answer.

1. $3 \times 5 =$ _____

$3 \times 50 =$ _____

$3 \times 500 =$ _____

2. $12 \div 4 =$ _____

$120 \div 4 =$ _____

$1200 \div 4 =$ _____

Write <, >, or =. Use the table to help you.

1 pt = 2c
1 qt = 2 pt, or 4 c
1 gal = 4 qt

3. 1 gal ◯ 4 qt

4. 1 pt ◯ 1 c

5. 1 qt ◯ 1 gal

6. 2 qt ◯ 2 c

7. 4 qt ◯ 6 pt

8. 2 qt ◯ 8 c

Solve. Make a list if it helps you.

9. Baron rides his bicycle to school. How many different paths can Baron take that are less than 3.5 miles?

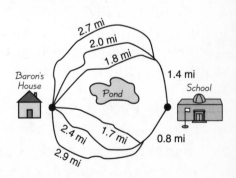

Baron's House

2.7 mi
2.0 mi
1.8 mi
1.4 mi
School
Pond
2.4 mi
1.7 mi
0.8 mi
2.9 mi

_____

Name _____

Write *slide, flip,* or *half turn*.

1.   **2.**

_____   _____

Write the decimals from least to greatest.

3. 2.3, 3.2, 2.5   _____

4. 5.8, 8.0, 5.0   _____

5. 0.4, 4.1, 4.0   _____

6. 10.5, 10.0, 0.5   _____

Solve each problem.

| 1 qt = 4 c |
| 1 pt = 2 c |

7. Mr. Abbot needs 2 quarts of water to make soup. He is using a cup to measure. How many times must he fill the cup?

_____

8. Megan uses 6 cups of juice to make lemonade. Her measuring cup holds 1 pint. How many times must she fill the measuring cup?

_____

Name _____

**Write the product. Use mental math
when you can.**

1.	32	2.	48	3.	15
	× 3		× 2		× 5

4.	35	5.	18	6.	45
	× 3		× 6		× 4

**Write >, <, or =. Use Fraction Bars to
help you.**

7. $\frac{7}{8}$ ◯ $\frac{5}{8}$ 8. $\frac{2}{3}$ ◯ $\frac{1}{4}$ 9. $\frac{2}{6}$ ◯ $\frac{1}{3}$

10. $\frac{2}{4}$ ◯ $\frac{1}{2}$ 11. $\frac{3}{10}$ ◯ $\frac{9}{10}$ 12. $\frac{4}{6}$ ◯ $\frac{1}{2}$

Complete the table to solve the problem.

13. Damian sells shell necklaces
for $12 each. He needs $45
to buy new sneakers. How
many necklaces must he sell? _____

Necklaces	1	2	3	4	5
Earnings	$12	$24			

148 DAILY CUMULATIVE REVIEW

Write the product. Use mental math.

1. $6 \times 3 \times 4 =$ _____   **2.** $5 \times 4 \times 6 =$ _____

3. $6 \times 2 \times 8 =$ _____   **4.** $9 \times 0 \times 7 =$ _____

Estimate. Which has a difference of:

5. about 100? _____   **6.** about 600? _____

a.   675   **b.**   998   **c.**   712
       $- 562$ $- 209$ $- 196$

Use the schedule to solve each problem.

7. Ying needs 45 minutes to get to the movies. If he leaves home at 12:30, will he get there in time to see *Star Flight*?

Movie Schedule	
Time	Movie
1:10	Star Flight
1:24	Circus Life
1:45	The Jungle
1:59	Cartoon Fun

_____

8. *Circus Life* is 30 minutes long. Can Ying see that movie and be in time for *Cartoon Fun*?

_____

Name _____

Estimate the product. Circle *a*, *b*, or *c*.

1. 3×105
   a. 30
   b. 300
   c. 3000

2. 3×23
   a. 60
   b. 600
   c. 6000

3. $2 \times \$5.12$
   a. $10
   b. $100
   c. $1000

Write the decimal.

4. two and four tenths   **5.** 6 and 1 tenth

_____   _____

6. one and nine tenths   **7.** $\frac{5}{10}$

_____   _____

Solve each problem. Remember, some problems may not have enough information.

8. Loren buys a book with a $5 bill. Her change is 72¢. The clerk gives Loren 6 coins. What are the coins?

_____

9. Len wants to buy a glove for $18 and a baseball. Can he buy both with $20?

_____

Name _____

Write the sum or difference.

1.	2.4	2.	0.8	3.	7.2
	+ 1.8		+ 4.9		+ 0.8

4.	6.4	5.	7.1	6.	5.0
	− 2.8		− 1.5		− 0.9

Write the perimeter.

7.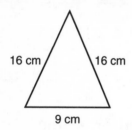

16 cm   16 cm

9 cm

_____

8.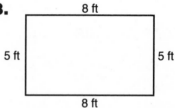

8 ft

5 ft   5 ft

8 ft

_____

Complete the table to solve the problem.

9. The coach wants to buy
   T-shirts for the team. The
   cost of each T-shirt is $15.
   The coach has $70. How
   many T-shirts can she buy?   _____

T-shirts	1	2	3	4	5
Cost	$15				

Name _____

Use a ruler to draw the line segment.

1. 4 cm

2. 8 cm

3. 1 dm

Write the product.

4.	340	**5.**	600	**6.**	264
	× 3		× 2		× 5

7.	205	**8.**	315	**9.**	175
	× 6		× 4		× 3

Solve each problem.

10. Mrs. Cutler is buying school supplies. Each box of pens costs $4.55. What will 3 boxes of pens cost?

_____

11. Mr. Perez orders 4 reams of drawing paper. Each ream has 250 sheets. How many sheets of paper will Mr. Perez get?

_____

Name _____

Next to each figure draw one that is the same size and shape.

1.

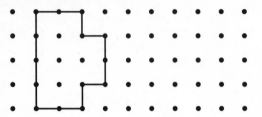

2.

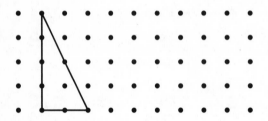

Use the pattern to complete the table. Then use the table to write the equivalent weight.

3.

lb	1	2	3	4	5	6	7
oz	16	32	48				

4. 2 lb = _____ oz   **5.** 4 lb = _____ oz

6. 96 oz = _____ lb   **7.** 16 oz = _____ lb

8. 32 oz = _____ lb   **9.** 3 lb = _____ oz

DAILY CUMULATIVE REVIEW

Write the value of the digit 6 in the number.

1. 560 _____ **2.** 76 _____

3. 680 _____ **4.** 2165 _____

5. 6109 _____ **6.** 5016 _____

Write the money amount. Use a dollar sign and decimal point.

7. six dollars and forty-eight cents _____

8. 12 dollars and 8 cents _____

9. twenty dollars and five cents _____

Solve.

10. Roberto bought three items. He paid with a $10 bill and got $1.82 in change. Which items did Roberto buy?

Animal Book $3.45

Magnifying Glass $2.59

Plant Book $2.70

Neon Glue $2.89

Name _____

154 DAILY CUMULATIVE REVIEW

Write *line, line segment,* or *neither*.

1.  **2.**

_____   _____

Write *parallel* or *not parallel*.

3. **4.**

_____   _____

Write the missing factor.

5. _____ × 8 = 64   **6.** 6 × _____ = 42

7. _____ × 5 = 35   **8.** 9 × _____ = 27

9. _____ × 8 = 8   **10.** _____ × 6 = 0

Solve.

11. Jane spins each
spinner and adds
the two numbers.
What are all the
possible sums?

_____

Name _____

 155 **DAILY CUMULATIVE REVIEW**
....

Write the quotient.

1. $5\overline{)25}$ **2.** $8\overline{)40}$ **3.** $9\overline{)36}$

4. $7\overline{)49}$ **5.** $3\overline{)24}$ **6.** $9\overline{)54}$

Write the product.

7. $\begin{array}{r} 243 \\ \times\quad 3 \\ \hline \end{array}$ **8.** $\begin{array}{r} 512 \\ \times\quad 2 \\ \hline \end{array}$ **9.** $\begin{array}{r} \$4.06 \\ \times\quad 3 \\ \hline \end{array}$

10. $\begin{array}{r} 314 \\ \times\quad 2 \\ \hline \end{array}$ **11.** $\begin{array}{r} 236 \\ \times\quad 4 \\ \hline \end{array}$ **12.** $\begin{array}{r} \$1.68 \\ \times\quad 5 \\ \hline \end{array}$

Solve the problem.

13. At Pizza Palace you can
choose from four pizza
toppings: broccoli, peppers,
mushrooms, and onions.
How many different
combinations of two
toppings can you have on
your pizza?   _____

156 DAILY CUMULATIVE REVIEW

Estimate the product. Circle *a*, *b*, or *c*.

1. 56
× 3

2. 321
× 2

3. 212
× 6

a. 15
b. 150
c. 1500

a. 60
b. 600
c. 6000

a. 12
b. 120
c. 1200

Write a fraction for the shaded part of each set. Then write a fraction for the unshaded part.

4.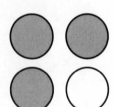

5.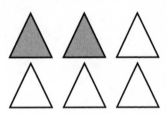

_____   _____

Solve the problem.

6. Clyde has a box of 12 crayons. One third of the crayons are broken. How many of Clyde's crayons are broken?

_____

Name _____

Write the decimals from least to greatest.

1. 0.3, 1.0, 3.0, 3.1 _____

2. 5.5, 8.3, 4.5, 5.4 _____

3. 16.3, 16.0, 15.7, 17.1 _____

4. 12.9, 11.2, 13.5, 5.9 _____

Write the quotient and the remainder.

5. $4\overline{)34}$ **6.** $5\overline{)28}$ **7.** $6\overline{)20}$

8. $3\overline{)19}$ **9.** $2\overline{)15}$ **10.** $8\overline{)50}$

Solve the problem.

11. There are 25 students and 4 teachers going on a camping trip. Each van carries 5 people. How many vans are needed? _____

158 DAILY CUMULATIVE REVIEW

Write the product.

1. $2 \times 65 =$ _____   **2.** $3 \times 84 =$ _____

3. $5 \times \$2.50 =$ _____   **4.** $4 \times \$0.86 =$ _____

Estimate which quotient is greater. Write *a* or *b*.

5. a. $4\overline{)51}$ **6. a.** $3\overline{)47}$

   b. $4\overline{)49}$ **b.** $2\overline{)47}$

_____   _____

Write the quotient and remainder.

7. $5\overline{)56}$ **8.** $7\overline{)89}$ **9.** $3\overline{)52}$

Solve.

10. Marie is decorating T-shirts. She decorates each T-shirt with 6 buttons. If Marie has 26 buttons, how many T-shirts can she decorate? _____

DAILY CUMULATIVE REVIEW

Choose the best estimate.
Circle *a*, *b*, or *c*.

1. 642 ÷ 7
   a. 70–80
   b. 90–100
   c. 40–50

2. 157 ÷ 5
   a. 10–20
   b. 50–60
   c. 30–40

Write how much time has passed.

3.

_____

Solve each problem.

4. Abdul painted his room from 9:30 to 11:00 this morning. Then he painted from 1:00 P.M. until 3:30 P.M. How long did Abdul paint?

5. At the hardware store, Abdul wants to buy a new paintbrush for $6 and a paint tray for two and a half dollars. Abdul has $10. Does he have enough money?

_____

160 DAILY CUMULATIVE REVIEW

Divide. Check your answer.

1. $5\overline{)256}$ **2.** $3\overline{)228}$ **3.** $4\overline{)252}$

4. $4\overline{)167}$ **5.** $6\overline{)336}$ **6.** $8\overline{)475}$

Estimate. About what fraction of the flag is shaded? Write $\frac{1}{4}$, $\frac{1}{2}$, or $\frac{3}{4}$.

7.   **8.**   **9.**

_____   _____   _____

Solve.

10. Which is the
better buy?   _____

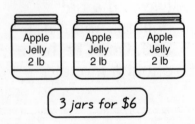

3 jars for $6

2 jars for $6